Autodesk
AutoCAD Architecture 2016
Fundamentals

Elise Moss

AUTODESK.
Authorized Author

Publications

SDC Publications
P.O. Box 1334
Mission, KS 66222
913-262-2664
www.SDCpublications.com
Publisher: Stephen Schroff

Examination Copies
Books received as examination copies are for review purposes only and may not be made available for student use. Resale of examination copies is prohibited.

Electronic Files
Any electronic files associated with this book are licensed to the original user only. These files may not be transferred to any other party.

Trademarks
The following are registered trademarks of Autodesk, Inc.: AutoCAD, Architectural Desktop, Inventor, Autodesk, AutoLISP, AutoCAD Design Center, Autodesk Device Interface, and HEIDI. Microsoft, Windows, Word, and Excel are either registered trademarks or trademarks of Microsoft Corporation. All other trademarks are trademarks of their respective holders.

The author and publisher of this book have used their best efforts in preparing this book. These efforts include the development, research and testing of the material presented. The author and publisher shall not be liable in any event for incidental or consequential damages with, or arising out of, the furnishing, performance, or use of the material.

ISBN-13: 978-1-58503-965-4
ISBN-10: 1-58503-965-9

Printed and bound in the United States of America.

Preface

No textbook can cover all the features in any software application. This textbook is meant for beginning users who want to gain a familiarity with the tools and interface of AutoCAD Architecture before they start exploring on their own. By the end of the text, users should feel comfortable enough to create a standard model, and even know how to customize the interface for their own use. Knowledge of basic AutoCAD and its commands is helpful, but not required. I do try to explain as I go, but for the sake of brevity I concentrate on the tools specific to and within AutoCAD Architecture.

The files used in this text are accessible from the Internet from the book's page on the publisher's website: www.SDCpublications.com. They are free and available to students and teachers alike.

We value customer input. Please contact us with any comments, questions, or concerns about this text.

Elise Moss
elise_moss@mossdesigns.com

Acknowledgements from Elise Moss

This book would not have been possible without the support of some key Autodesk employees.

The effort and support of the editorial and production staff of SDC Publications is gratefully acknowledged. I especially thank Stephen Schroff for his helpful suggestions regarding the format of this text.

Finally, truly infinite thanks to Ari for his encouragement and his faith.

- Elise Moss

About the Author

Elise Moss has worked for the past thirty years as a mechanical designer in Silicon Valley, primarily creating sheet metal designs. She has written articles for Autodesk's Toplines magazine, AUGI's PaperSpace, DigitalCAD.com and Tenlinks.com. She is President of Moss Designs, creating custom applications and designs for corporate clients. She has taught CAD classes at DeAnza College, Silicon Valley College, and for Autodesk resellers. She is currently teaching CAD at Laney College in Oakland. Autodesk has named her as a Faculty of Distinction for the curriculum she has developed for Autodesk products. She holds a baccalaureate degree in Mechanical Engineering from San Jose State.

She is married with three sons. Her older son, Benjamin, is an electrical engineer. Her middle son, Daniel, works with AutoCAD Architecture in the construction industry. His designs have been featured in architectural journals. Her youngest son, Isaiah, is in college, but shows signs of being a budding engineer. Her husband, Ari, is retired from a distinguished career in software development.

Elise is a third generation engineer. Her father, Robert Moss, was a metallurgical engineer in the aerospace industry. Her grandfather, Solomon Kupperman, was a civil engineer for the City of Chicago.

She can be contacted via email at elise_moss@mossdesigns.com.

More information about the author and her work can be found on her website at www.mossdesigns.com.

Autodesk®
Certified Instructor

Other books by Elise Moss
Autodesk Revit Architecture 2016 Basics
AutoCAD 2016 Fundamentals

Table of Contents

Lesson 1:
Desktop Features

AutoCAD Architecture (ACA) enlists object oriented process systems (OOPS). That means that ACA uses intelligent objects to create a building. This is similar to using blocks in AutoCAD. Objects in AutoCAD Architecture are blocks on steroids. They have intelligence already embedded into them. A wall is not just a collection of lines. It represents a real wall. It can be constrained, has thickness and material properties, and is automatically included in your building schedule.

AEC is an acronym for Architectural/Engineering/Construction.
BID is an acronym for Building Industrial Design.
BIM is an acronym for Building Information Modeling.
AIA is an acronym for the American Institute of Architects.
MEP is an acronym for Mechanical/Electrical/Plumbing.

The following table describes the key features of objects in AutoCAD Architecture:

Feature Type	Description
AEC Camera	Create perspective views from various camera angles. Create avi files.
AEC Profiles	Create AEC objects using polylines to build doors, windows, etc.
Anchors and Layouts	Define a spatial relationship between objects. Create a layout of anchors on a curve or a grid to set a pattern of anchored objects, such as doors or columns.
Annotation	Set up special arrows, leaders, bar scales.
Ceiling Grids	Create reflected ceiling plans with grid layouts.
Column Grids	Define rectangular and radial building grids with columns and bubbles.
Design Center	Customize your AEC block library.
Display System	Control views for each AEC object.
Doors and Windows	Create custom door and window styles or use standard objects provided with the software.
Elevations and Sections	An elevation is basically a section view of a floor plan.
Layer Manager	Create layer standards based on AIA CAD Standards. Create groups of layers. Manage layers intelligently using Layer Filters.
Masking Blocks	Store a mask using a polyline object and attach to AEC objects to hide graphics
Model Explorer	View a model and manage the content easily. Attach names to mass elements to assist in design.
Multi-view blocks	Blocks have embedded defined views to allow you to easily change view.

Feature Type	Description
Railings	Create or apply different railing styles to a stair or along a defined path.
Roofs	Create and apply various roof styles.
Floorplate slices	Generate the perimeter geometry of a building.
Spaces and Boundaries	Spaces and boundaries can include floor thickness, room height, and wall thickness.
Stairs	Create and apply various stair types.
Tags and Schedules	Place tags on objects to generate schedules. Schedules will automatically update when tags are modified, added, or deleted.
Template Files	Use templates to save time. Create a template with standard layers, text styles, linetypes, dimension styles, etc.
Walls	Create wall styles to determine material composition. Define end caps to control opening and end conditions. Define wall interference conditions.

AutoCAD Architecture sits on top of AutoCAD. It is helpful for users to have a basic understanding of AutoCAD before moving to AutoCAD Architecture. Users should be familiar with the following:

- AutoCAD toolbars and ribbons
- Zoom and move around the screen
- Manage blocks
- *Draw* and *Modify* commands
- *Model* and *Paper space* (layout),
- Dimensioning and how to create/modify a dimension style

If you are not familiar with these topics, you can still move forward with learning AutoCAD Architecture, but you may find it helpful to have a good AutoCAD textbook as reference in case you get stuck.

The best way to use AutoCAD Architecture is start your project with massing tools (outside-in design) or space planning tools (inside-out design) and continue through to construction documentation.

The AEC Project Process Model

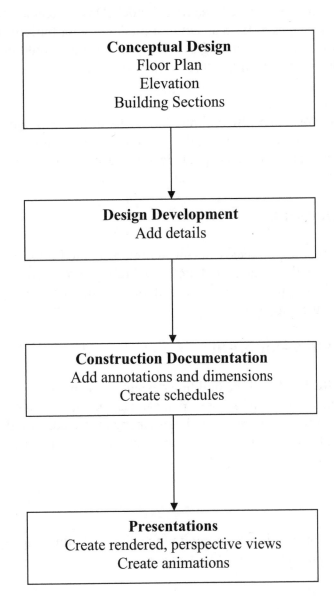

Conceptual Design

In the initial design phase, you can assemble AutoCAD Architecture mass elements as simple architectural shapes to form an exterior model of your building project. You can also lay out interior areas by arranging general spaces as you would in a bubble diagram. You can manipulate and consolidate three-dimensional mass elements into massing studies.

Later in this phase, you can create building footprints from the massing study by slicing floorplates, and you can begin defining the structure by converting space boundaries into walls. At the completion of the conceptual design phase, you have developed a workable schematic floor plan.

Design Development

As you refine the building project, you can add more detailed information to the schematic design. Use the features in AutoCAD Architecture to continue developing the design of the building project by organizing, defining, and assigning specific styles and attributes to building components.

Construction Development

After you have fully developed the building design, you can annotate your drawings with reference marks, notes, and dimensions. You can also add tags or labels associated with objects. Information from the objects and tags can be extracted, sorted, and compiled into schedules, reports, tables, and inventories for comprehensive and accurate construction documentation.

Presentations

A major part of any project is presenting it to the client. At this stage, you develop renderings, animations, and perspective views.

If you use the **QNEW** tool, it will automatically use the template set in the Options dialog.

Express Tools

By default, Express Tools are not installed with AutoCAD Architecture. If for some reason, you are missing the Express Tools you can modify the installation to add them.

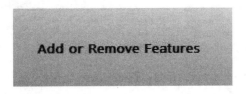

Go to the Control Panel, select **AutoCAD Architecture 2016** and select **Uninstall/Change**. Then select **Add or Remove Features**.

Press **Next** to skip this screen.

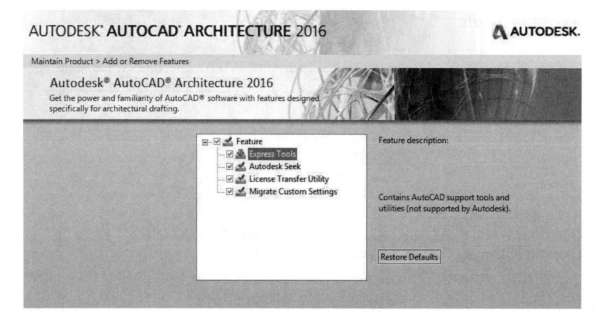

Place a check next to Express Tools to enable the installation and continue with the installation. Press **Update**.

Express Tools can be used to create custom line types, control layers, and many other useful functions.

If you forgot to install the Express Tools, they can be installed at any time. You don't need the Express Tools to run AutoCAD Architecture or to use this textbook. They just are useful for a lot of users.

Exercise 1-1:
Setting the Template for QNEW

Drawing Name: New
Estimated Time: 15 minutes

This exercise reinforces the following skills:

- ❑   Use of templates
- ❑   Getting the user familiar with tools and the ACA environment

1.   Launch ACA.

Select the drop-down arrow next to the large A to access the Application Menu.

Select **New→Drawing**.

Select the desired template to use.

Each template controls units, layers, and plot settings.

Select *Aec Model (Imperial.Ctb)*.

This template uses Imperial units (feet and inches and a Color Table to control plot settings).

Press **Open.**

2.   Place your cursor on the command line.

Right click the mouse.

Select **Options** from the short-cut menu.

3.   Select the **Files** tab.
     Locate the *Template Settings* folder.

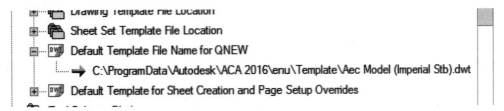

Click on the + symbol to expand.
Locate the Default Template File Name for QNEW.

4.   Highlight the path and file name listed and select the **Browse** button.

5. Browse to the *Template* folder.

This should be listed under
Documents & Settings\[user name]\Application Data\ Autodesk\ACA 2016\enu
or
Program Data/Autodesk/ ACA 2016/enu

6.   Locate the *Aec Model (Imperial Ctb).dwt [Aec Model (Metric Ctb).dwt]* file.

Press **Open**.

7. Note that you can also set where you can direct the user for templates. This is useful if you want to create standard templates and place them on a network server for all users to access.

You can also use this setting to help you locate where your template files are located.

8. Press **Apply** and **OK**.

9. Select the **QNEW** tool button.

10. Note that you have tabs for all the open drawings. You can switch between any open drawing files by selecting the folder tab.

11. Type **units** on the *Command* line.

Notice how you get a selection of commands as you type.

Press ENTER to select UNITS.

12. Note that the units are in inches [millimeters].

The units are determined by the template you set to start your new drawing.

13. Close the drawing without saving.

Templates can be used to preset layers, property set definitions, dimension styles, units, and layouts.

AEC Drawing Options

Menu	Tools→Options
Command line	Options
Context Menu→Options	Place Mouse in the graphics area and right click
Shortcut	Place mouse in the command line and right click

Access the Options dialog box.

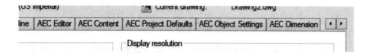

ACA's Options includes five additional AEC specific tabs.
They are AEC Editor, AEC Content, AEC Object Settings, AEC Dimension, and AEC Project Defaults.

AEC Editor

Diagnostic Messages	All diagnostic messages are turned off by default.
Similar-Purpose Dialogs	Options for the position of dialog boxes and viewers.
Use Common Position	Sets one common position on the screen for similar dialog boxes, such as door, wall, and window add or modify dialog boxes. Some dialog boxes, such as those for styles and properties, are always displayed in the center of the screen, regardless of this setting.
Use Common Viewer Position and Sizes	Sets one size and position on the screen for the similar-purpose viewers in AutoCAD Architecture. Viewer position is separately controlled for add, modify, style, and properties dialog boxes.
Optimize for Speed	Options for display representations and layer loading in the Layer Manager dialog.
Object Snap	Enable to limit certain display representations to respond only to the Node and Insert object snaps. This setting affects stair, railing, space boundary, multi-view block, masking block, slice, and clip volume result (building section) objects.
Apply Common Property Sets to New Objects	Property sets are used for the creation of schedule tables. Each AEC object has embedded property sets, such as width and height, to be used in its schedule. AEC properties are similar to attributes. Size is a common property across most AEC objects. Occasionally, you may use a tool on an existing object and the result may be that you replace the existing object with an entirely different object. For example, if you apply the tool properties of a door to an existing window, a new door object will replace the existing window. When enabled, any property sets that were assigned to the existing window will automatically be preserved and applied to the new door provided that the property set definitions make sense.
Solution Tips Problem: The walls are overlapping. Possible Solution: Remove the overlapping wall(s).	Users can set whether they wish a solution tip to appear while they are drafting or plotting. A solution tip identifies a drafting error and suggests a solution.
Dynamic Dimensions Linetype	Set the linetype to be used when creating dynamic dimensions. This makes it easier to distinguish between dynamic and applied dimensions. You may select either continuous or dot linetypes.

Export to AutoCAD	Enable Bind Xrefs.
Export to AutoCAD ☑ Bind xrefs ☑ Use Insert Method when Binding xrefs Filename Prefix: Filename Suffix: [ACAD-] [ ]	If you enable this option, the xref will be inserted as a block and not an xref. Enable Use Insert Method when binding Xrefs if you want all objects from an xref drawing referenced in the file you export to be automatically exploded into the host drawing. If you enable this option, the drawing names of the xref drawings are discarded when the exported drawing is created. In addition, their layers and styles are incorporated into the host drawing. For example, all exploded walls, regardless of their source (host or xref) are located on the same layer. Disable Use Insert Method when binding Xrefs if you want to retain the xref identities, such as layer names, when you export a file to AutoCAD or to a DXF file. For example, the blocks that define walls in the host drawing are located on A-Wall in the exploded drawing. Walls in an attached xref drawing are located on a layer whose name is created from the drawing name and the layer name, such as Drawing1|WallA. Many architects automatically bind and explode their xrefs when sending drawings to customers to protect their intellectual property. Enter a prefix or a suffix to be added to the drawing filename when the drawing is exported to an AutoCAD drawing or a DXF file. In order for any of these options to apply, you have to use the Export to AutoCAD command. This is available under the Files menu.
Unselected Grip Colors	Assign the colors for each type of grip.

Units for Legacy Drawings	Determines the units to be used when opening an AutoCAD drawing in AutoCAD Architecture.
	  Automatic – uses the current AutoCAD Architecture units setting
	  Imperial – uses Imperial units
	  Metric – uses Metric units

Option Settings are applied to your current drawing and saved as the default settings for new drawings. Because AutoCAD Architecture operates in a Multiple Document Interface, each drawing stores the Options Settings used when it was created and last saved. Some users get confused because they open an existing drawing and it will not behave according to the current Options Settings.

AEC Content

Architectural Object Style Path	Allows you to specify a path of source files to be used to import object styles; usually used for system styles like walls, floors, or roofs
AEC DesignCenter Content Path	Type the path and location of your content files, or click Browse to search for the content files.
Tool Catalog Content Root Path	Type the path and location of your Tool Catalog files, or click Browse to search for the content files.
IFC Content Path	Type the path and location of your Tool Catalog files, or click Browse to search for the content files.
Detail Component Databases	Select the **Add/Remove** button to set the search paths for your detail component files.
Keynote Databases	Select the **Add/Remove** button to set the search paths for your keynote database files.
Display Edit Schedule Data Dialog During Tag Insertion	To attach schedule data to objects when you insert a schedule tag in the drawing, this should be ENABLED.

IFC Content is an object-based building data model that is non-proprietary. It uses open-source code developed by the IAI (International Alliance for Interoperability) to promote data exchange between CAD software. IFC Content might be created in Autodesk Revit, Inventor, or some other software for use in your projects.

Using AEC Content

AutoCAD Architecture uses several pre-defined and user-customizable content including:

- ❑ Architectural Display Configurations
- ❑ Architectural Profiles of Geometric Shapes
- ❑ Wall Styles and Endcap geometry
- ❑ Door styles
- ❑ Window styles
- ❑ Stair styles
- ❑ Space styles
- ❑ Schedule tables

Standard style content is stored in the AEC templates subdirectory. You can create additional content, import and export styles between drawings.

AEC Object Settings

Wall Settings	
Autosnap New Wall Justification Lines	Enable to have the endpoint of a new wall that is drawn within the Autosnap Radius of the baseline of an existing wall automatically snap to that baseline. If you select this option and set your Autosnap Radius to 0, then only walls that touch, clean up with each other.
Autosnap Grip Edited Wall Justification Lines	Enable to snap the endpoint of a wall that you grip edit within the Autosnap Radius of the baseline of an existing wall. If you select this option and set your Autosnap Radius to 0, then only walls that touch clean up with each other.
Autosnap Radius	Enter a value to set the snap tolerance.
Do not display opening end cap styles	Enable Do Not Display Opening Endcap Styles to suppress the display of endcaps applied to openings in walls. Enabling this option boosts drawing performance when the drawing contains many complex endcaps.
Stair Settings	
Presentation Format (No Cut Lines or Path)	If this is enabled, a jagged line and directional arrows will not display.

Node Osnap	Determines which snap is enabled when creating stairs:
	    Vertical Alignment
	    Flight and Landing Corners

Measure Stair Height	Rough floor to floor – ignore offsets Finished floor to floor – include top and bottom offsets
Calculator Limits	Strict – stair will display a defect symbol when an edit results in a violation of the Calculation rules. Relaxed – no defect symbol will be displayed when the stair violates the Calculation rules. The Calculation rules determine how many treads are required based on the riser height and the overall height of the stairs.

AEC Display Resolution 	This determines the resolution of arcs and circular elements. Facet Deviation – The default is ½″. Facet Maximum – this can be set from 100 to 10,000. Higher settings use more memory and may affect screen refresh rates.
Space Settings	If *Automatically update associative spaces* is enabled, AutoCAD Architecture will automatically determine which spaces are adjacent to each other and update their association accordingly. The Maximum Gap Size is the allowable distance between spaces. The Maximum Automatic Adjacency sets the gap allowance between spaces for spaces to be considered adjacent. The Floor Boundary Thickness sets the value of the Floor Boundary Thickness. The Calculation Standard determines how the space values are calculated.
AEC Property Set Definitions	Enable Automatically Attach to attach property set data to objects that you want to include in a schedule table or link to schedule tags. By default, this option is disabled, which means you would have to manually attach property set data to elements when the property set data is modified or created.

AEC Dimension

General	
Update Added/Removed points immediately	Enable to update the display every time you add or remove a point from a dimension chain.
Make Manual Dimension Points Associative	Enable if you want the dimension to update when the object is modified.
Override Display of Undefined Text	Enable to automatically underline each manually overridden dimension value.
Underline All	Enable to manually underline overridden dimension values.
Underline None	Enable to not underline any overridden dimension value.
Units	
Dimension in:	Select the desired units from the drop-down list.
Use Superscript mm	If your units are set to meters or centimeters, enable superscripted text to display the millimeters as superscript. 4.34^{20}
Trailing Zero Suppression for Superscript	To suppress zeros at the end of superscripted numbers, select Trailing Zeros Suppression for Superscript. You can select this option only if you have selected Use Superscript mm and your units are metric.

	4.12³ ⬛⬛⬛⬛⬛⬛⬛⬛⬛
Automatic Scale of AutoCAD Dimstyles	Select the dimstyles you would like to automatically scale when units are reset.
Elevation Labels	Select the unit in which elevation labels are to be displayed. This unit can differ from the drawing unit.
Display +/- for 0.00 Values	
Display + for Positive Values	
Dimension Label Prefixes	 Dimension Label Prefixes are set based on the object selected from the drop-down. You can set label prefixes for Doors, Windows, Openings, and Stairs. Select the object, and then set the prefix for each designation. The designations will change based on the object selected.

AEC Project Defaults

Most BID/AEC firms work in a team environment where they divide a project's tasks among several different users. The AEC Project Defaults allows the CAD Manager or team leader to select a folder on the company's server to locate files; set up template files with the project's title blocks; and even set up a webpage to post project information.

Select paths, file names and file locations:
- ⊟ 🖳 AEC Project Location Search Path
  - ⇨ C:\Users\elise\Dropbox\ACAD Arch 2014\ACA 2014 exercises
- ⊟ 📑 Default Project Template Files
  - ⊞ 📄 Construct Template File
  - ⊞ 📄 Element Template File

To add a path, simply expand the folder and use the Browse button to locate the desired folder.

You can add more than one path to the AEC Project Location Search Path. All the other folders only allow you to have a single location for template files, the project bulletin board, and the default project image.

I highly recommend that you store any custom content in a separate directory as far away from AutoCAD Architecture as possible. This will allow you to back up your custom work easily and prevent accidental erasure if you upgrade your software application.

You should be aware that AutoCAD Architecture currently allows the user to specify only ONE path for custom content, so drawings with custom commands will only work if they reside in the specified path.

☐ Close project drawings when switching projects	If enabled, when a user switches projects in the Project Navigator, any open drawings not related to the new project selected will be closed. This conserves memory resources.
☑ Show detailed drawing preview when dropping view on sheet	If enabled, then the user will see the entire view as it is being positioned on a sheet. If it is disabled, the user will just see the boundary of the view for the purposes of placing it on a sheet.
☐ Show Project Browser at startup	If enabled, you will automatically have access to the Project Browser whenever you start AutoCAD Architecture.

Accessing the Project Browser

Command line	AECProjectBrowser
Quick Access Toolbar	
Files Menu	Project Browser

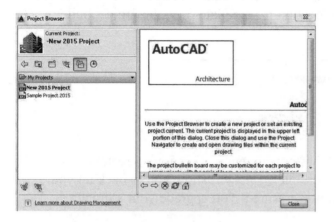

The Project Browser allows you to manage your project. Projects have two parts: the building model and the reports generated from the building model.

The building model is made of two drawing types: constructs and elements. A construct is any unique portion of a building. It can be a flight of stairs, a specific room, or an entire floor. Constructs are assigned to a level (floor) and a division within a project. Elements are any AEC object or content that is used multiple times in a model. For example, furniture layouts or lavatory layouts. Elements can be converted into constructs if you decide that they will not be used repeatedly.

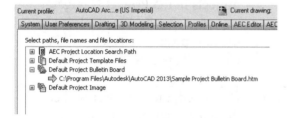

The text you see in the right window is actually an html file. The path to this file is controlled in the path for the Default Project Bulletin Board. This is set on the AEC Project Defaults tab in the Options dialog.

Architectural Profiles of Geometric Shapes

You can create mass elements to define the shape and configuration of your preliminary study, or mass model. After you create the mass elements you need, you can change their size as necessary to reflect the building design.

- **Mass element**: A single object that has behaviors based on its shape. For example, you can set the width, depth, and height of a box mass element, and the radius and height of a cylinder mass element.

Mass elements are parametric, which allows each of the shapes to have very specific behavior when it comes to the manipulation of each mass element's shape. For example, if the corner grip point of a box is selected and dragged, then the width and depth are modified. It is easy to change the shape to another form by right-clicking on the element and selecting a new shape from the list.

Through Boolean operations (addition, subtraction, intersection), mass elements can be combined into a mass group. The mass group provides a representation of your building during the concept phase of your project.

- **Mass group**: Takes the shape of the mass elements and is placed on a separate layer from the mass elements.
- **Mass model**: A virtual mass object, shaped from mass elements, which defines the basic structure and proportion of your building. A marker appears as a small box in your drawing to which you attach mass elements.

As you continue developing your mass model, you can combine mass elements into mass groups and create complex building shapes through addition, subtraction, or intersection of mass elements. You can still edit individual mass elements attached to a mass group to further refine the building model.

To study alternative design schemes, you can create a number of mass element references. When you change the original of the referenced mass element, all the instances of the mass element references are updated.

The mass model that you create with mass elements and mass groups is a refinement of your original idea that you carry forward into the next phase of the project, in which you change the mass study into floor plates and then into walls. The walls are used to start the design phase.

Mass Elements are accessed from the Home ribbon.

Mass Elements that can be defined from the ribbon include Arches, Gables, Doric Columns, etc.

The Style Manager

Access the Style Manager from the Manage ribbon.

The Style Manager is a Microsoft® Windows Explorer-based utility that provides you with a central location in Autodesk AutoCAD Architecture where you can view and work with styles in drawings or from Internet and intranet sites.

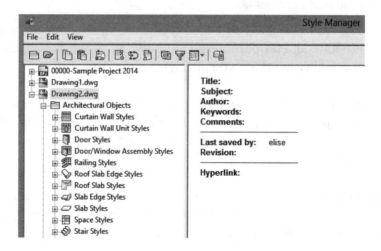

Styles are sets of parameters that you can assign to objects in Autodesk AutoCAD Architecture to determine their appearance or function. For example, a door style in Autodesk AutoCAD Architecture determines what door type, such as single or double, bi-fold or hinged, a door in a drawing represents. You can assign one style to more than one object, and you can modify the style to change all the objects that are assigned that style.

Depending on your design projects, either you or your CAD Manager might want to customize existing styles or create new styles. The Style Manager allows you to easily create, customize, and share styles with other users. With the Style Manager, you can:

- Provide a central point for accessing styles from open drawings and Internet and intranet sites

- Quickly set up new drawings and templates by copying styles from other drawings or templates

- Sort and view the styles in your drawings and templates by drawing or by style type

- Preview an object with a selected style

- Create new styles and edit existing styles

- Delete unused styles from drawings and templates

- Send styles to other Autodesk AutoCAD Architecture users by email

Objects in Autodesk AutoCAD Architecture that use styles include 2D sections and elevations, AEC polygons, curtain walls, curtain wall units, doors, endcaps, railings, roof slab edges, roof slabs, schedule tables, slab edges, slabs, spaces, stairs, structural members, wall modifiers, walls, window assemblies, and windows.

Additionally, layer key styles, schedule data formats, and cleanup group, mask block, multi-view block, profile, and property set definitions are handled by the Style Manager.

Most of the objects in Autodesk AutoCAD Architecture have a default Standard style. In addition, Autodesk AutoCAD Architecture includes a starter set of styles that you can use with your drawings. The Autodesk AutoCAD Architecture templates contain some of these styles. Any drawing that you start from one of the templates includes these styles.

You can also access the styles for doors, end caps, spaces, stairs, walls, and windows from drawings located in *Documents and Settings\All Users\ Application Data\Autodesk\...\Styles\Imperial or Metric*. Property set definitions and schedule tables are located in the *Documents and Settings\All Users\Application Data\ Autodesk...\AEC Content\ Imperial\ Documentation\Schedule Tags* folder.

Exercise 1-2:
Creating a New Geometric Profile

Drawing Name: New
Estimated Time: 15 minutes

This exercise reinforces the following skills:

- ❑ Use of AEC Design Content
- ❑ Use of Mass Elements
- ❑ Use of Views
- ❑ Visual Styles
- ❑ Modify using Properties

Creating an arch mass element

1.   Start a New Drawing.

2.   [▢]   Select the QNEW tool from the Standard toolbar.

3.   Because we assigned a template in Exercise 1-1, a drawing file opens without
     prompting us to select a template.

All the massing tools are available
on the **Home** ribbon in the Build
section.

4.   [Arch]   Select the **Arch** tool from the Massing drop down list.

5.   Expand the **Dimensions** section on the Properties palette.

Set Specify on screen to **No**.
Set the Width to **2′ [600]**.
Set the Depth to **6″ [200]**.
Set the Height to **1′ 6″ [500]**.
Set the Radius to **6″ [200]**.

6.   Pick a point anywhere in the drawing area.

Press ENTER to accept a Rotation Angle of 0 or right click and select **ENTER**.

Press **ENTER** to exit the command.

7.   Switch to an isometric view.

To switch to an isometric view, simply go to **View** Ribbon. Under the Views list, select **SW Isometric**.

Our model so far.

8.

Select **Realistic** on the View ribbon under Face Effects to shade the model.

You can also type **SHA** on the command line, then **R** for Realistic.

9. To change the arch properties, select the arch so that it is highlighted. If the properties dialog doesn't pop up automatically, right click and select **Properties**.

10.

Change the Radius to **9″** [**250**].

Pick into the graphics window and the arch will update.

11. Press **ESC** to release the grips on the arch.

12. Save the drawing as *ex1-2.dwg*.

If you see this dialog, it means that the mass element just created (the arch) cannot be saved as a previous version file.

Press **Close**.

 Visual Styles are stored with the drawing.

Exercise 1-3:

Creating a New Visual Style

Drawing Name: ex1-2.dwg
Estimated Time: 15 minutes

This exercise reinforces the following skills:

- ❑ Workspaces
- ❑ Use of Visual Styles
- ❑ Controlling the Display of Objects

1. Open *ex1-2.dwg*.

2.   Activate the **View** ribbon.

3.   Launch the Visual Styles Manager.

    To launch, select the small arrow in the lower right corner of the Visual Styles panel.

4. 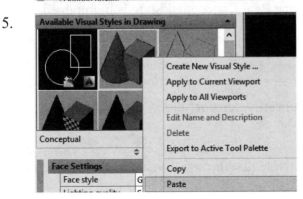   Highlight the **Conceptual** tool.

    Right click and select **Copy**.

5. Right click and select **Paste**.

6.   Highlight the copied tool.
Right click and select **Edit Name and Description**.

7.   Change the name and description to **Real Conceptual**.

Press **OK**.

8.   Under Face Settings:
Set Material display to **Materials and textures**.

9.   Under Face Settings:

Set the Face Style to **Realistic**.

Under Environment Settings:

Set the Backgrounds to **Off**.

Under Edge Settings:

Set the Show to **None**.

10.   Verify that the Real Conceptual Style is highlighted/selected.

Right click and select the **Apply to Current Viewport** tool.

[−][Custom View][Real Conceptual]

Note that the active visual style is listed in the upper right corner of the drawing.

11.   Save the drawing as *ex1-3.dwg*.

Exercise 1-4:

Creating an Autodesk 360 Account

Drawing Name: (none, start from scratch)
Estimated Time: 5 Minutes

This exercise reinforces the following skills:

❑   Create an account on Autodesk 360.

You must have an internet connection to access the Autodesk server.

1. Next to the Help icon at the top of the screen:

    Select **Sign In to Autodesk 360**.

2. If you have an existing Autodesk ID, you can use it.

    If not, select the link that says **Need an Autodesk ID**.

    You may have an existing Autodesk ID if you have registered Autodesk software in the past.
    Autodesk 360 is free to students and educators. For other users, you are provided a small amount of initial storage space for free.

    I like my students to have a 360 account because it will automatically back up their work.

3. Fill in the form to create an Autodesk ID account.

    Be sure to write down the ID you select and the password.

4.

Once the account is created, you will be asked to log in to your account.

There will be a slight pause while the server validates the log in.

You will then be asked to check your settings.

You can automatically save your work to the Cloud.
If you do this, you will be able to access your files anywhere you have internet access.

Press **OK**.

5. You will see the name you selected as your Autodesk ID in the Cloud sign-in area.

Use your Autodesk 360 account to create renderings, back-up files to the Cloud so you can access your drawings on any internet-connected device, and to share your drawings.

Exercise 1-5:

Creating a New Wall Style

Drawing Name: New using Imperial [Metric] (ctb).dwt
Estimated Time: 30 minutes

This exercise reinforces the following skills:

❑ Style Manager
❑ Use of Wall Styles

1. Select the **QNEW** tool from the Standard toolbar.

2. Activate the **Manage** ribbon.

Select the **Style Manager** from the **Style & Display** panel.

3. The Style Manager is displayed, with the current drawing expanded in the tree view. The wall styles in the current drawing are displayed under the wall style type. All other style and definition types are filtered out in the tree view.

    Locate the wall styles in the active drawing.

4.   Highlight Wall Styles by left clicking on the name. Right click and select **New**.

5. Change the name of the new style by typing **Brick_Block**.

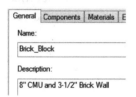

6. In the General tab, type in the description **8″ CMU and 3-1/2″ [200 mm CMU and 90 mm] Brick Wall** in the Description field as shown.

7. Select the Components tab.
    Change the Name to **CMU** by typing in the Name field indicated.

    Press the dropdown arrow next to the Edge Offset Button.
    Set the Edge Offset to 0.

Index	Name	Priority	Width	Edge Offset	Function	Dimension	
1	CMU	1	BW	0	Structural	☑	☐

8. A 0 edge offset specifies that the outside edge of the CMU is coincident with the wall baseline.

9. Press the **Width** down arrow button.

Set the value to **-3″** **[-80]**.

    This specifies that the CMU has a fixed width of 3 inches [80 mm] in the negative direction from the wall baseline (to the inside).

    You now have one component defined for your wall named CMU with the properties shown.

10. Press the **Add** Component button on the right side of the dialog box. Next, we'll add wall insulation.

11. In the Name field, type **Insulation**.

Set the Priority to 1. (The lower the priority number, the higher the priority when creating intersections.)

Set the Edge Offset with a value of **0**.

Set the Component Width as shown, with a value of **1.5″** [38] and the Base Width set to 0.

This specifies that the insulation has a fixed width of 1.5″ [38 mm] offset in a positive direction from the wall baseline (to the outside).

12. Set the Function to **Non-Structural**.

Index	Name	Priority	Width	Edge Offset	Function
1	CMU	1	-3"+ BW	0"	Structural
2	Insulation	1	1 1/2"+ BW	0"	Non-Structural

13. Note that the preview changes to show the insulation component.

14.   Now, we add an air space component to our wall. Press the **Add Component** button.

15. Rename the new component **Air Space**.

  Set the Edge Offset to **0**.

This specifies that the inside edge of the air space is coincident with the outside edge of the insulation.

The width should be set to **1″ [25.4] + Base Width**.

This specifies that the air gap will have a fixed width of 1 inch [25.4 mm] offset in the positive direction from the wall baseline (to the outside).

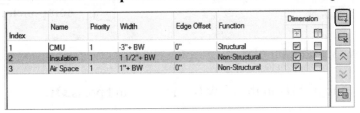

16. Use the **Add Component** tool to add the fourth component.

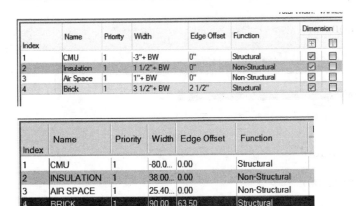

The Name should be **Brick**.
The Priority set to **1**.
The Edge Offset set to **2.5″ [63.5]**.
The Width set to **3.5″ [90]**.

The Function should be set to **Structural**.

Index	Name	Priority	Width	Edge Offset	Function	Dimension	
1	CMU	1	-3″+ BW	0″	Structural	☑	☐
2	Insulation	1	1 1/2″+ BW	0″	Non-Structural	☑	☐
3	Air Space	1	1″+ BW	0″	Non-Structural	☑	☐
4	Brick	1	3 1/2″+ BW	2 1/2″	Structural	☑	☐

Index	Name	Priority	Width	Edge Offset	Function	
1	CMU	1	-80.0...	0.00	Structural	
2	INSULATION	1	38.00...	0.00	Non-Structural	
3	AIR SPACE	1	25.40...	0.00	Non-Structural	
4	BRICK	1	90.00...	63.50	Structural	

Total Width: VARIES

	Name	Priority	Width	Edge Offset	Function	Dimension			Bottom Offset
Index						⊞	⬚⬚	⊟	
1	CMU	1	-3"	0"	Structural	☑	☑	☑	0"
2	Insulation	1	1 1/2"	0"	Non-Structural	☐	☐	☐	0"
3	Air Space	1	1"+ BW	0"	Non-Structural	☐	☐	☐	0"
4	Brick	1	3 1/2"	2 1/2"	Structural	☑	☑	☑	0"

17. The Dimension section allows you to define where the extension lines for your dimension will be placed when measuring the wall. In this case, we are not interested in including the air space or insulation in our linear dimensions. Uncheck those boxes.

18. 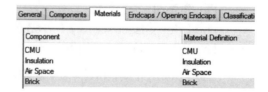 Note how your wall style previews.

If you right click in the preview pane, you can change the preview window by zooming, panning, or assigning a Preset View.

The preview pane uses a DWF-style interface.

19. Select the **Materials** tab.

Highlight the **CMU** component.

Select the **Add New Material** tool.

20. Enter **CMU** in the New Name field and press **OK**.

21. Use the **Add New Material** tool to assign new materials to each component.

22. Highlight the **CMU** Component.

Select the **Edit Material** tool.

23. Select the **Display Properties** tab.

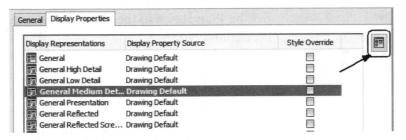

Highlight the **General Medium Detail** Display Representation.

Click on the **Style Override** button.

24. Select the **Hatching** tab.

    Highlight **Plan Hatch** and select **Pattern**.

    Under Type, select **Predefined**.

    Under Pattern Name, select **AR-CONC**.

25. Assign the **AR-CONC** Pattern to
    all the Display Components.

    Set the Angles to **0**.

26. Press **OK** twice to return to the Materials tab of the Wall Properties dialog.

27. 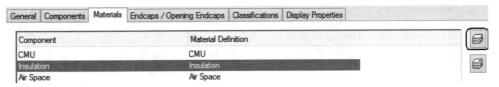 Highlight **Insulation** and select the **Edit Material** tool.

28. Select the **Display Properties** tab.

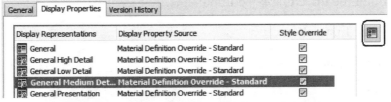

Click on the **Style Override** button.

Highlight the **General Medium Detail** Display Property.

29. Select the **Hatching** tab.

    Select all the Display Components so they all are highlighted.

30. 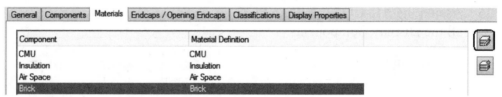 Set the Plan Hatch to the **INSUL** pattern under Predefined type.

Set the Angle to **0.00**.

31. Verify that a check is placed in the Style Override button.

32. Press **OK** to return to the previous dialog.

33. Highlight **Brick** and select the **Edit Material** tool.

34. Select the **Display Properties** tab.

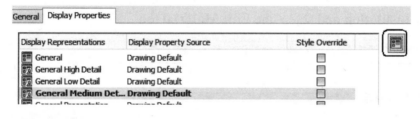

Highlight the **General Medium Detail** Display Representation.

Click on the **Style Override** button.

35. Select the **Hatching** tab.

Highlight the three display components.

Select the first pattern.

36. Set the Type to **Predefined**.

37. Select the **Browse** button.

38. Select the **BRSTONE** pattern.

39.   Set the Angle to 0 for all hatches.

Press **OK** twice.

40.   Activate the Components tab. Highlight each component and use the << >> arrows to position the component. By shifting each component position, you can see where it is located. Locate the Brick so it is on the Exterior side and the CMU so it is interior.

☑ Auto Calculate Edge Offset

You can also use the Auto Calculatte Edge Offset option to ensure all the components are correct.

41.   Close the Style Manager.

Press **OK** to exit the Edit dialog.
You can preview how the changes you made to the material display will appear when you create your wall.

42. Save as *ex1-4.dwg*.

Exercise 1-6
Creating a Tool

Drawing Name: ex1-4.dwg
Estimated Time: 15 minutes

This exercise reinforces the following skills:

- ❑   Use of AEC Design Content
- ❑   Use of Wall Styles

1.   Open or continue working in *ex1-4.dwg*.

2.   Activate the Home ribbon.

Select **Tools→Design Tools** to launch the tool palette.

3.   Activate the Walls palette by right clicking on the tabs and selecting **Walls**.

4.   On the Walls tool palette:

Select the **Settings** button.

5.   Select **View Options**.

6. Adjust the Image Size and select the desired View style.

You can apply the preference to the Current Palette (the walls palette only) or all palettes.

Press **OK**.

7. Verify that the tool palette is open with the Walls palette active.

8. Activate the **Manage** ribbon.

Style Manager

Select the **Style Manager** tool.

9. Wall Styles
    Brick_Block
    Standard

Locate the **Brick-Block** wall style you created in the Style Manager.

10. Drag and drop the wall style onto your Walls palette.

Press **OK** to close the Style Manager.

11.   Highlight the **Brick_Block** tool.
Right click and select **Rename**.

12.   Change the name to **8″ CMU- 3.5″ Brick [200 mm CMU – 90 mm]**.

13.   Select the new tool and draw a wall.
You may draw a wall simply by picking two points.
If you enable the ORTHO button on the bottom of the screen, your wall will be straight.

14.   Select the wall you drew.

Right click and select **Properties**.

Note that the wall is placed on the A-Wall Layer and uses the Brick-Block Style you defined.

15.   Save your file as *Styles.dwg*.

The wall style you created will not be available in any new drawings unless you copy it over to the default template.

 To make it easy to locate your exercise files, browse to where the files are located when you save the file. Right click on the left pane and select Add Current Folder.

Exercise 1-7:

Copying a Style to a Template

Drawing Name: Styles1.dwg, Imperial (Metric).ctb.dwt
Estimated Time: 20 minutes

This exercise reinforces the following skills:

- Style Manager
- Use of Templates
- Properties dialog

1.   Close any open drawings.

Go to the Application menu and select
Close → All Drawings.

2.   Start a New Drawing using QNEW.

3.   Activate the **Manage** ribbon.

Style
Manager l   Select the **Style Manager** tool.

4.   Select the **File Open** tool in the Style Manager dialog.

5.   Locate the *styles.dwg* you created.
Select **Open**.

File name: Styles
Files of type: Drawing (*.dwg)

Note: Make sure the Files of type is set to dwg or you will not see your files.

6. Styles is now listed in the Style Manager.

7. Select the **File Open** tool.

8. Set the Files of type to ***Drawing Template (*.dwt)***.

9. *You should automatically be directed to the Template folder.*

   Browse to the *Template* folder.

10. Locate the *AEC Model Imperial (Metric) Ctb.dwt* file.
    Press **Open**.

    This is the default template we selected for QNEW.

11. You should see files open in the Style Manager.

12. Locate the **Brick_Block** Wall Style in the *Styles.dwg*.

13. Right click and select **Copy**.

14. Locate Wall Styles under the template drawing.

    Highlight, right click and select **Paste**.

15. 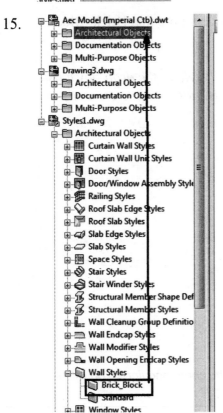 You could also just drag and drop the Brick_block style from the Styles file to the template.

16. Apply   Press **Apply**.

17. The following drawing has changed.
    C:\ProgramData\Autodesk\ACA
    2015\enu\Template\Aec Model (Imperial
    Ctb).dwt

    Do you wish to save changes to this file?

    Press **Yes**.

18. Close the Style Manager.

19. Drawing1*   Look at the drawing folder tabs. The Styles.dwg and the template drawing are not shown. These are only open in the Style Manager.

20. Select the **QNEW** tool.

21.   Activate the Home ribbon.

                          Select the **Wall** tool.

22.   The Properties dialog should pop up when the WallAdd tool is selected.

In the Style drop-down list, note that Brick_Block is available.

If you don't see the wall style in the drop-down list, verify that you set the default template correctly in Options.

23.   Press Escape to end the WallAdd command.

24.   Close all drawing files without saving.

A fast way to close all open files is to type CLOSEALL on the command line. You will be prompted to save any unsaved files.

Layer Manager

Back in the days of vellum and pencil, drafters would use separate sheets to organize their drawings, so one sheet might have the floor plan, one sheet the site plan, etc. The layers of paper would be placed on top of each other and the transparent quality of the vellum would allow the drafter to see the details on the lower sheets. Different colored pencils would be used to make it easier for the drafter to locate and identify elements of a drawing, such as dimensions, electrical outlets, water lines, etc.

When drafting moved to Computer Aided Design, the concept of sheets was transferred to the use of Layers. Drafters could assign a Layer Name, color, linetype, etc. and then place different elements on the appropriate layer.

AutoCAD Architecture has a Layer Management system to allow the user to implement AIA standards easily.

Layer Manager

The Layer Manager helps you organize, sort, and group layers, as well as save and coordinate layering schemes. You can also use layering standards with the Layer Manager to better organize the layers in your drawings.

When you open the Layer Manager, all the layers in the current drawing are displayed in the right panel. You can work with individual layers to:

- Change layer properties by selecting the property icons

- Make a layer the current layer

- Create, rename, and delete layers

If you are working with drawings that contain large numbers of layers, you can improve the speed at which the Layer Manager loads layers when you open it by selecting the Layer Manager/Optimize for Speed option in your AEC Editor options.

The Layer Manager has a tool bar as shown.

	Layer Standards You can import Layer Standards from an existing drawing or Export Layer Standards using the current drawing. 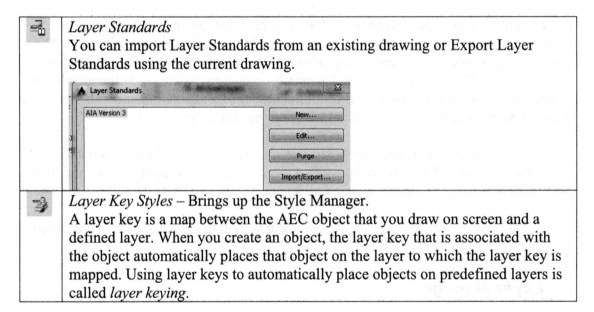
	Layer Key Styles – Brings up the Style Manager. A layer key is a map between the AEC object that you draw on screen and a defined layer. When you create an object, the layer key that is associated with the object automatically places that object on the layer to which the layer key is mapped. Using layer keys to automatically place objects on predefined layers is called *layer keying*.

The layer key styles in Autodesk AutoCAD Architecture, Release 3 and above replace the use of LY files. If you have LY files from S8 or Release 1 of AutoCAD Architecture that you want to use, then you can create a new layer key style from an LY file. On the command line enter **-AecLYImport** to import legacy LY files.

	Layer Key Overrides
	You can apply overrides to any layer keys within a layer key style that is based on a layer standard. The structure of the layer name of each layer that each layer key maps an object to is determined by the descriptive fields in the layer standard definition. You can override the information in each field according to the values set in the layer standard definition. You can allow overrides on all the layer keys within a layer key style, or you can select individual layer keys that you want to override. You can also choose to allow all of the descriptive fields that make up the layer name to be overridden, or you can specify which descriptive fields you want to override.
	Load Filter Groups
	This tool allows you to load a saved filter group.
	Save Filter Groups
	This tool allows you to save a defined filter group, so that you can use it in other drawings.
	New Layer
	Creates a new layer.
	New Layer from Standard
	Creates a new layer based on an existing layer standard. 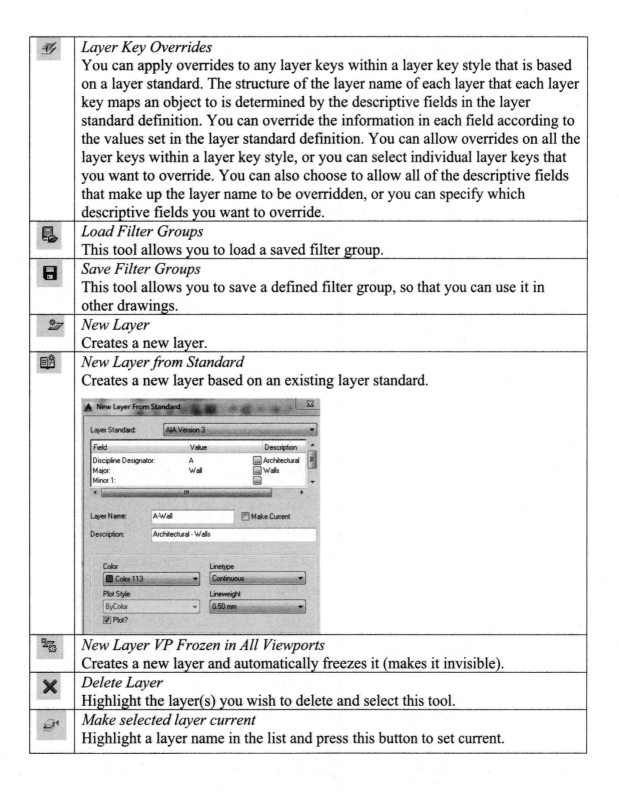
	New Layer VP Frozen in All Viewports
	Creates a new layer and automatically freezes it (makes it invisible).
	Delete Layer
	Highlight the layer(s) you wish to delete and select this tool.
	Make selected layer current
	Highlight a layer name in the list and press this button to set current.

The following are the default layer keys used by Autodesk AutoCAD Architecture when you create AEC objects.

Default layer keys for creating AEC objects

Layer Key	Description	Layer Key	Description
ANNDTOBJ	Detail marks	COMMUN	Communication
ANNELKEY	Elevation Marks	CONTROL	Control systems
ANNELOBJ	Elevation objects	CWLAYOUT	Curtain walls
ANNMASK	Masking objects	CWUNIT	Curtain wall units
ANNMATCH	Match Lines	DIMLINE	Dimensions
ANNOBJ	Notes, leaders, etc.	DIMMAN	Dimensions (AutoCAD points)
ANNREV	Revisions	DOOR	Doors
ANNSXKEY	Section marks	DOORNO	Door tags
ANNSXOBJ	Section marks	DRAINAGE	Drainage
ANNSYMOBJ	Annotation marks	ELEC	Electric
APPL	Appliances	ELECNO	Electrical tags
AREA	Areas	ELEV	Elevations
AREAGRP	Area groups	ELEVAT	Elevators
AREAGRPNO	Area group tags	ELEVHIDE	Elevations (2D)
AREANO	Area tags	EQUIP	Equipment
CAMERA	Cameras	EQUIPNO	Equipment tags
CASE	Casework	FINCEIL	Ceiling tags
CASENO	Casework tags	FINE	Details- Fine lines
CEILGRID	Ceiling grids	FINFLOOR	Finish tags
CEILOBJ	Ceiling objects	FIRE	Fire system equip.
CHASE	Chases	FURN	Furniture
COGO	Control Points	FURNNO	Furniture tags
COLUMN	Columns	GRIDBUB	Plan grid bubbles

Layer Key	Description	Layer Key	Description
GRIDLINE	Column grids	SITE	Site
HATCH	Detail-Hatch lines	SLAB	Slabs
HIDDEN	Hidden Lines	SPACEBDRY	Space boundaries
LAYGRID	Layout grids	SPACENO	Space tags
LIGHTCLG	Ceiling lighting	SPACEOBJ	Space objects
LIGHTW	Wall lighting	STAIR	Stairs
MASSELEM	Massing elements	STAIRH	Stair handrails
MASSGRPS	Massing groups	STRUCTBEAM	Structural beams
MASSSLCE	Massing slices	STRUCTBEAMIDEN	Structural beam tags
MED	Medium Lines	STRUCTBRACE	Structural braces
OPENING	Wall openings	STRUCTBRACEIDEN	Structural brace tags
PEOPLE	People	STRUCTCOLS	Structural columns
PFIXT	Plumbing fixtures	STRUCTCOLSIDEN	Structural column tags
PLANTS	Plants - outdoor	SWITCH	Electrical switches
PLANTSI	Plants - indoor	TITTEXT	Border and title block
POLYGON	AEC Polygons	TOILACC	Arch. specialties
POWER	Electrical power	TOILNO	Toilet tags
PRCL	Property Line	UTIL	Site utilities
PRK-SYM	Parking symbols	VEHICLES	Vehicles
ROOF	Rooflines	WALL	Walls
ROOFSLAB	Roof slabs	WALLFIRE	Fire wall patterning
ROOMNO	Room tags	WALLNO	Wall tags
SCHEDOBJ	Schedule tables	WIND	Windows
SEATNO	Seating tags	WINDASSEM	Window assemblies
SECT	Miscellaneous sections	WINDNO	Window tags
SECTHIDE	Sections (2D)		

Desktop Display Manager

Exercise 1-8:
Exploring the Display Manager

Drawing Name: display_manager.dwg
Estimated Time: 15 minutes

This exercise reinforces the following skills:

❑   Display Manager

1.   Open *display_manager.dwg*.

2.   Access the **Display Manager** from the Manage ribbon.

3.   The display system in Autodesk® AutoCAD Architecture controls how AEC objects are displayed in a designated viewport. By specifying the AEC objects you want to display in a viewport and the direction from which you want to view them, you can produce different architectural display settings, such as floor plans, reflected plans, elevations, 3D models, or schematic displays.

4. Expand the *Representations by Object* folder.

Locate Door.

You see that there are different ways a door will appear depending on the display configuration selected.

Highlight **Threshold Plan**.

5. You see that the Threshold visibilities are turned off.

6. Highlight the **Plan** configuration.

7. 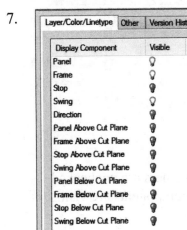 You see that some door components are turned on and others are turned off.

8. Highlight the Model configuration.

9. 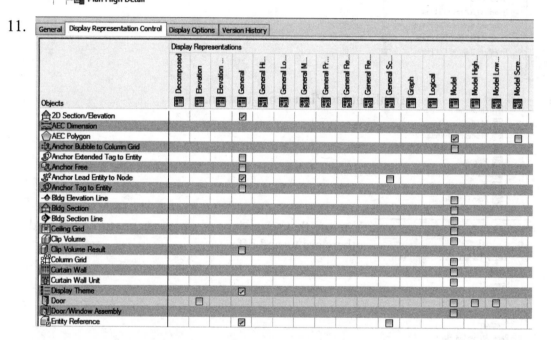 You see that some door components are turned on and others are turned off.

10. Go to the Sets folder. The Set highlighted in bold is the active Display Representation.

    Highlight **Plan**.

11. Select the Display Representation Control tab.
Locate **Door** under Objects.
Note that some display representations are checked and others are unchecked.
A check indicates that the door is visible. Which door components are visible is controlled under Representations by Object.

The three different folders – Configurations, Sets, and Representations by Object – are different ways of looking at the same elements. Each folder organizes the elements in a different way. If you change the display setting in one folder, it updates in the other two folders.

12. Expand the **Configurations** folder.

13. Expand **Medium Detail**.
You see the different display sets. Note that Medium Detail does not hold all the different display sets. You can add or remove display sets.
Close the Display Manager.

14. Close the drawing without saving.

Exercise 1-9:

Creating a Text Style

Drawing Name: new using QNEW
Estimated Time: 15 minutes

This exercise reinforces the following skills:

❑   CUI – Custom User Interface
❑   Ribbon
❑   Panel
❑   Tab

1.   Start a new drawing using the QNEW tool.

2.   Select the Text Style tool on the Home ribbon.

It is located on the Annotation panel under the drop-down.

3.

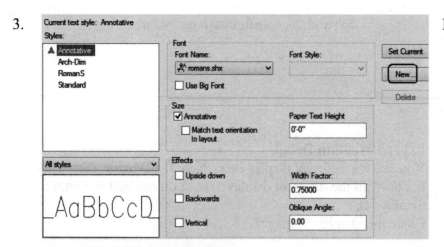

Press the **New** button in the Text Styles dialog box.

4.

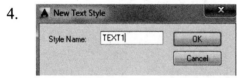

In the New Text Style dialog box, enter **TEXT1** for the name of the new text style and press **OK**.

5.

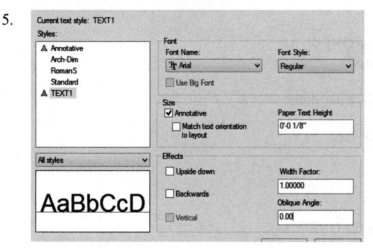

Fill in the remaining information in the Text Style dialog box as shown.

Set the Font Name to **Arial**.
Set the Font Style to **Regular**.
Set the Paper Text Height to **1/8″**.
Set the Width Factor to **1.00**.

6. Press the Apply button first and then the Close button to apply the changes to TEXT1 and then close the dialog box.

7. Save as *fonts.dwg*.

- ➢ You can use PURGE to eliminate any unused text styles from your drawing.
- ➢ You can import text styles from one drawing to another using the Design Center.
- ➢ You can store text styles in your template for easier access.
- ➢ You can use any Windows font to create AutoCAD Text.

Exercise 1-10
Project Settings

Drawing Name: new using QNEW
Estimated Time: 5 minutes

This exercise reinforces the following skills:

❑ Project Navigator
❑ Project Path Options

In order for tags on windows, doors, etc. to work properly, you must assign your building model to a project.

1.
Start a new drawing by pressing the + tab.

2. Right click in the command window and select **Options**.

3. Select the **AEC Project Defaults** tab.

4. Set the AEC Project Location Search Path to the location where you are saving your files.

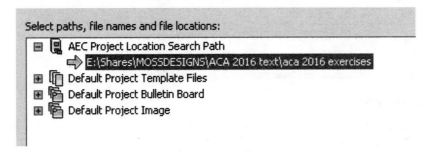

Select paths, file names and file locations:

⊟ 🗐 AEC Project Location Search Path
  ⇨ E:\Shares\MOSSDESIGNS\ACA 2016 text\aca 2016 exercises
⊞ 📑 Default Project Template Files
⊞ 📑 Default Project Bulletin Board
⊞ 📑 Default Project Image

Close the dialog.

5. Launch the **Project Navigator** from the Quick Access toolbar.

6. Launch the **Project Browser** using the toolbar on the bottom of the Project Navigator palette.

7. 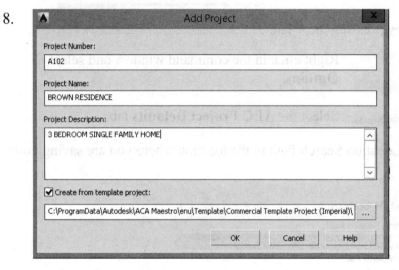   Select the **New Project** tool.

8. Type **A102** for the Project Number.

   Type **Brown Residence** for the Project Name.

   Enter a project description.

   Press **OK**.

9. Close the Project Browser.

10. Save as *ex1-8.dwg*.

Lesson 2:
Site Plans

Most architectural projects start with a site plan. The site plan indicates the property lines, the house location, a North symbol, any streets surrounding the property, topographical features, location of sewer, gas, and/or electrical lines (assuming they are below ground – above ground connections are not shown), and topographical features.

When laying out the floor plan for the house, many architects take into consideration the path of the sun (to optimize natural light), street access (to locate the driveway), and any noise factors. AutoCAD Architecture includes the ability to perform sun studies on your models.

AutoCAD Architecture allows the user to simulate the natural path of the sun based on the longitude and latitude coordinates of the site, so you can test how natural light will affect various house orientations.

A plot plan must include the following features:

- ❑ Length and bearing of each property line
- ❑ Location, outline, and size of buildings on the site
- ❑ Contour of the land
- ❑ Elevation of property corners and contour lines
- ❑ North symbol
- ❑ Trees, shrubs, streams, and other topological items
- ❑ Streets, sidewalks, driveways, and patios
- ❑ Location of utilities
- ❑ Easements and drainages (if any)
- ❑ Well, septic, sewage line, and underground cables
- ❑ Fences and retaining walls
- ❑ Lot number and/or address of the site
- ❑ Scale of the drawing

The plot plan is drawn using information provided by the county/city and/or a licensed surveyor.

When drafting with pencil and vellum, the drafter will draw to a scale, such as $\frac{1}{8}'' = 1'$, but with AutoCAD Architecture, you draw full-size and then set up your layout to the proper scale. This insures that all items you draw will fit together properly. This also is important if you collaborate with outside firms. For example, if you want to send your files to a firm that does HVAC, you want their equipment to fit properly in your design. If everyone drafts 1:1 or full-size, then you can ensure there are no interferences or conflicts.

Exercise 2-1:
Creating Custom Line Types

Drawing Name: New
Estimated Time: 15 minutes

This exercise reinforces the following skills:

- ❑ Creation of linetypes
- ❑ Customization

Architectural drafting requires a variety of custom linetypes in order to display specific features. The standard linetypes provided with AutoCAD Architecture are insufficient from an architectural point of view. You may find custom linetypes on Autodesk's website, www.cadalog.com, or any number of websites on the Internet. However, the ability to create linetypes as needed is an excellent skill for an architectural drafter.

It's a good idea to store any custom linetypes in a separate file. The standard file for storing linetypes is acad.lin. If you store any custom linetypes in acad.lin file, you will lose them the next time you upgrade your software.

1. *Once the Express Tools are installed, you can start this exercise. Refer to Lesson 1 for instructions on how to install the Express Tools. If you are unable to install the Express Tools, you can skip this lesson and use the custom file included with the file downloads.*

     To verify that the Express Tools are installed, simply look at your ribbon headings.

2. Start a new drawing using **QNEW**.

3. ———————————— ——————— ———————— ——————————————

    Draw a property line.
    This property line was created as follows:
        Set ORTHO ON.
        Draw a horizontal line 100 units long.

    Use SNAP FROM to start the next line @30,0 distance from the previous line.
    You can also simply use object tracking to locate the next line.
    The short line is 60 units long.
    Use SNAP FROM to start the next line @30,0 distance from the previous line.
    The second short line is 60 units long.
    Use SNAP FROM to start the next line @30,0 distance from the previous line.
    Draw a second horizontal line 100 units long.

4. Activate the Express Tools ribbon.

Select the **Tools** drop-down.

Go to **Express→Tools→Make Linetype**.

5. Browse to the folder where you are storing your work.

 Create a file name called *custom-linetypes.lin* and press **Save**.

Place all your custom linetypes in a single drawing file and then use the AutoCAD Design Center to help you locate and load the desired linetype.

6. When prompted for the linetype name, type: property-line.
   When prompted for the linetype description, type: property-line.
   Specify starting point for line definition; select the far left point of the line type.
   Specify ending point for line definition; select the far right point of the line type.
   When prompted to select the objects, start at the long line on the left and pick the line segments in order.

7. Type **linetype** to launch the Linetype Manager.

8. 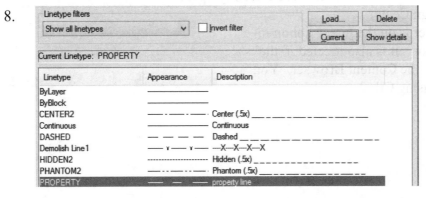 The linetype you created is listed.

Highlight the PROPERTY-LINE linetype and select CURRENT.

Press **OK**.

9. Draw some lines to see if they look OK. Make sure you make them long enough to see the dashes. If you don't see the dashes, adjust the linetype scale using Properties. Set the scale to 0.0125.

10. custom-linetypes Locate the *custom-linetypes.lin* file you created.

Open it using NotePad.

11.

*PROPERTY-LINE,property line
A,200,-60,120,-60,200,-60,120,-60,120

You see a description of the property-line.

12. Save as *ex2-1.dwg*.

Exercise 2-2:

Creating New Layers

Drawing Name: New

Estimated Time: 20 minutes

This exercise reinforces the following skills:

- ❑ Design Center
- ❑ Layer Manager
- ❑ Creating New Layers
- ❑ Loading Linetypes

1.   Start a new drawing using QNEW.

      Open Ex2-1.dwg.

2.   You should see two file tabs for the two drawings that are currently open.

3.   Launch the Design Center.
      The Design Center is on the Insert ribbon in the Content section. It is also located in the drop-down under the Content Browser. You can also launch using Ctl+2.

4. Select the **Open Drawings** tab.

Browse to the *Ex2-1.dwg* file.

Open the Linetypes folder.

Scroll to the **Property-line** linetype definition.

5. Highlight the PROPERTY-LINE linetype.

Drag and drop into your active window or simply drag it onto the open drawing listed.

6. Close the Design Center.

7. Activate the **Layer Manager** on the Home ribbon.

8. Note that several layers have already been created. The template automatically sets your Layer Standards to AIA.

9. Select the New Layer from Standard tool.

10.

Under Layer Standard, select **Non Standard**.

Name the layer **A-Site-Property-Lines**.

Set the Color to **Green**.

Select the **Property-Line** linetype.

Set the Lineweight to **Default**.

Enable **Plot**.
Press **Apply**.

11.

Create another layer.

Name the layer **A-Contour-Line**.

Set the color to **42**.

Select the linetype pane for the new linetype.

Press **Other**.

12.

Enable **Show Linetypes in File**.

Highlight **DASHEDX2** and press **OK** to assign it to the selected layer name.

13.

Note that the linetype was assigned properly.

Press **OK**.

14.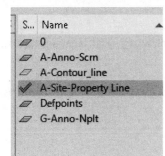

Set the A-Site-Property-Line layer current.

Highlight the layer name then select the green check mark to set current.

You can also double left click to set the layer current.

15. Right click on the header bar and select **Maximize all columns** to see all the properties for each layer.

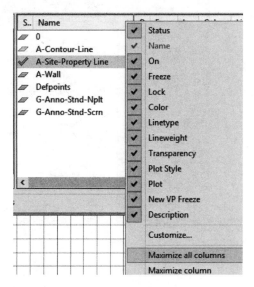

16. Use the X in the upper corner to close the Layer Manager.

17. Save as *Ex2-2.dwg*.

Exercise 2-3:

Creating a Site Plan

Drawing Name: Ex2-2.dwg
Estimated Time: 30 minutes

This exercise reinforces the following skills:

- ❑ Use of ribbons
- ❑ Documentation Tools
- ❑ Elevation Marks
- ❑ Surveyors' Angles

1. Open or continue working in *ex2-2.dwg*.

2.   Go to **Drawing Utilities→Drawing Setup**.

    This is located on the Applications Menu panel.

3.

Select the **Units** tab.
Set the Drawing Units to **Inches**.
Set up the Length Type to **Architectural**.
Set the Precision to ¼″.
Set the Angle Type to **Surveyors**.
Set the Precision to **N 0d00′ E**.
Press **Apply** and **OK**.

You can set your units as desired and then enable **Save As Default** ☐ Save As Default .
Then, all future drawings will use your unit settings.

4. Draw the property line shown on the **A-Site-Property-Lines** layer.

Specify first point: 1′,5′
Specify next point: @186′ 11″ < s80de
Specify next point: @75′<n30de
Specify next point: @125′11″<n
Specify next point: @250′<180

[186'11" 🔒] [S80DE]

This command sequence uses
Surveyor's Units.

Metric data entry using centimeters:

```
Specify first point: 12,60

Specify next point or [Undo]: @2243<s80de

Specify next point or [Undo]: @900<n30de

Specify next point or [Close/Undo]: @1511<n

Specify next point or [Close/Undo]: @3000<180

Specify next point or [Close/Undo]:
```

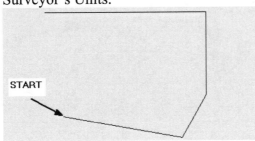

*You can use the TAB key to advance to
the surveyor unit box.*

Turn ORTHO off before creating the arc.

5. 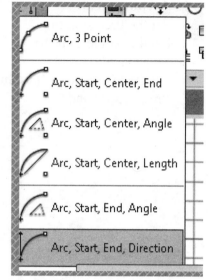 Draw an arc using Start, End, Direction to close the figure.

6.   Select the bottom point as the Start point.
Right click and select the End option.
Select the top point at the End point.
Click inside the figure to set the direction of the arc.

7.   Select the midpoint on the arc to activate the grip.
Press the Ctl key to cycle to the radius dimension.
Enter **192'** [58521.6].

8. Set the **A-Contour-Line layer** current.

9.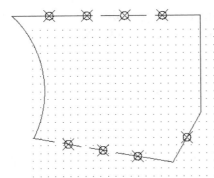

Use the **DIVIDE** command to place points as shown.

The top line is divided into five equal segments.

The bottom-angled line is divided into four equal segments.

The small angled line is divided into two equal segments.

10.

Type **DDPTYPE** to access the Point Style dialog or use the Point Style tool that was added to the Format tab on the ribbon in Lesson 1.

Go to **Format→Point Style** to set the points so they are visible.

Select the Point Style indicated.

Press **OK**.

11. Draw contour lines using **Pline** and **NODE** Osnaps as shown.

Be sure to put the contour lines on the contour line layer.

12. Type **qselect** on the *Command* line.

13.

Set the Object Type to **Point**.
Set the Color = Equals **ByLayer**.

Press **OK**.

14.

All the points are selected.
Right click and select **Basic Modify Tools→ Delete**.

15. Type UCSICON, OFF to turn off the UCS icon.

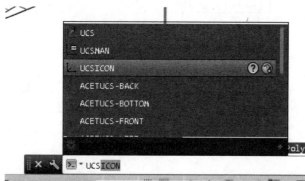

When you start typing in the command line, you will see a list of commands.

Use the up and down arrow keys on your keyboard to select the desired command.

16.   Activate the Design Tools palette on the Home ribbon.

17. 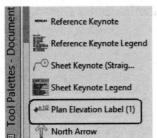 Right click on the gray bar on the palette to activate the short-cut menu.

Left click on **All Palettes** to enable the other palettes.

18. Activate the Annotation tab on the palette.

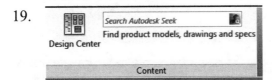 Locate the **Plan Elevation Label**, but it's not the type we need for a site plan.

Instead we'll have to add an elevation label from the Design Center to the Tool Palette.

19. 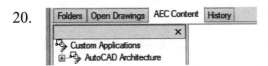 Type **Ctl+2** to launch the Design Center.
Or:
Activate the **Insert** ribbon.
Select the **Design Center** tool under Content.
Or:
Type **ADC**.

20. Select the **AEC Content** tab.

21. Browse to
Imperial/Documentation/Elevation Labels/ 2D Section.

[Metric/Documentation/Elevation Labels/2D Section].

22.

Locate the Elevation Label (1) file.

Highlight the elevation label.

Drag and drop onto the Tool Palette.

Close the Design Center.

23.

Select the Elevation Label on the Tool Palette.

Select the Endpoint shown.

24. Set the Elevation to **0″ [0.00]**.
Set the Prefix to **EL**.
Press **OK**.

25.

Zoom in to see the elevation label.

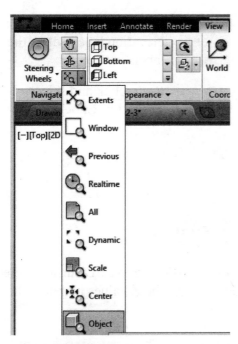

You can use the **Zoom Object** tool to zoom in quickly.

This is located on the View ribbon

The Elevation Label is automatically placed on the A-Anno-Dims layer.

To verify this, just select the label and look at the Layers panel on the Home ribbon.

26. EL ±0.00"   Place an elevation label on the upper left vertex as shown.

27.   Place labels as shown.

28.

Repeat ANNOELEVATIONLABELADD

Recent Input

Isolate Objects
Basic Modify Tools
Clipboard

AEC Modify Tools

Edit View Block Offsets
Edit Attributes
Annotative Object Scale

Add Selected
AEC Dimension

Select Component

Edit Object Display...

Elevation Label Modify...

Edit Multi-View Block Definition...

To modify the value of the elevation label, select the label.

Right click and select **Elevation Label Modify**.

29.

Geometry	
Start X	1'-0"
Start Y	5'-0"
Start Z	0"
End X	185'-0 15/16"
End Y	-27'-5 1/2"
End Z	2'-11"
Delta X	184'-0 15/16"
Delta Y	-32'-5 1/2"

To change the toposurface to a 3D surface, select each line and modify the Z values to match the elevations.

30.

Geometry	
Start X	185'-0 15/16"
Start Y	-27'-5 1/2"
Start Z	2'-11"
End X	222'-6 15/16"
End Y	37'-5 15/16"
End Z	3'-9"
Delta X	37'-6"
Delta Y	64'-11 7/16"
Delta Z	10"

31.

Geometry	
Start X	222'-6 15/16"
Start Y	37'-5 15/16"
Start Z	3'-9"
End X	222'-6 15/16"
End Y	163'-4 15/16"
End Z	3'-10"
Delta X	0"
Delta Y	125'-11"
Delta Z	1"
Length	125'-11"
Angle	90.00

32.

Geometry	
Start X	222'-6 15/16"
Start Y	163'-4 15/16"
Start Z	3'-10"
End X	-27'-5 1/16"
End Y	163'-4 15/16"
End Z	0"
Delta X	-250'-0"
Delta Y	0"
Delta Z	-3'-10"
Length	250'-0 11/32"

33. Use the ViewCube to inspect your toposurface and then return to a top view.

34. Open the *fonts.dwg*. This is the file you created in a previous exercise.

35. Type **Ctl+2** to launch the Design Center.

36. Browse to the Textstyles folder under the fonts.dwg.

37. Drag and drop the **Text1** text style into the drawing.

Close the Design Center.

38. Set **A-Anno-Dims** as the current Layer.

39. Set the Current Text Style to **TEXT1.**

N80

40. Select the **Single Line** text tool from the Home ribbon.

41.

If this dialog appears, set the scale to the same scale as the current view.

Select the midpoint of the line as the insertion point.
Right click and select **Justify**.
Set the Justification to **Center**.
Set the rotation angle to **–10** degrees
Use %%d to create the degree symbol.

42. To create the S60… note, use the **TEXT** command.

Use a rotation angle of 60 degrees.

When you are creating the text, it will preview horizontally. However, once you left click or hit ESCAPE to place it, it will automatically rotate to the correct position.

43. Create the **Due South 125′ 11″ [Due South 3840.48]**, with a rotation angle of 90 degrees.

Add the text shown on the top horizontal property line.

N 90° 250' E

44.

Add the Chord note shown.
Rotation angle is 90 degrees.

45.

Adjust the scale to **1/32″ = 1′-0″** to see the property line labels.

46. Save the file as *ex2-4.dwg*.

Exercise 2-4:

Creating a Layer User Group

Drawing Name: Ex 2-4.dwg
Estimated Time: 15 minutes

This exercise reinforces the following skills:

- ❏ Use of toolbars
- ❏ Layer Manager
- ❏ Layer User Group

A Layer User Group allows you to group your layers, so you can quickly freeze/thaw them, turn them ON/OFF, etc. *We can create a group of layers that are just used for the site plan and then freeze them when we don't need to see them.*

The difference between FREEZING a Layer and turning it OFF is that entities on FROZEN Layers are not included in REGENS.   Speed up your processing time by FREEZING layers.

1.   Open *ex2-4.dwg*.

2. Select the **Layer Manager** tool.

3.   Highlight the word **All** in the Filters pane.

    Right click and select the **New Group Filter**.

4. Name the group **Site Plan**.

5.

Highlight the Site Plan group.
Right click and select **Select Layers →
Add**.

6. Type **ALL** on the command line.
    This selects all the items in the drawing.
    Press **ENTER** to finish the selection.
    The layers are now listed in the Layer Manager under the Site Plan group.

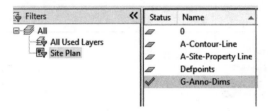

Close the Layer Manager.

7. We can use this group to quickly freeze, turn off, etc. the layers in the Site Plan group.

    Save the drawing as *ex2-5.dwg* and close.

QUIZ 1

True or False

1. Doors, windows, and walls are inserted into the drawing as objects.

2. The Architectural Toolbars are loaded from the ACA Menu Group.

3. To set the template used by the QNEW tool, use Options.

4. If you start a New Drawing using the 'QNew' tool shown above, the Start-Up dialog will appear unless you assign a template.

5. Mass elements are used to create Mass Models.

6. The Layer Manager is used to organize, sort, and group layers.

7. Layer Standards are set using the Layer Manager.

8. You must load a custom linetype before you can assign it to a layer.

Multiple Choice
Select the best answer.

9. If you start a drawing using one of the standard templates, AutoCAD Architecture will automatically create _____ layouts.

    A. A work layout plus Model Space
    B. Four layouts, plus Model Space
    C. Ten layouts, plus Model Space
    D. Eleven layouts, plus Model Space

10. Options are set through:

    A. Options
    B. Desktop
    C. User Settings
    D. Template

11. The Display Manager controls:

    A. How AEC objects are displayed in the graphics window
    B. The number of viewports
    C. The number of layout tabs
    D. Layers

12. Mass Elements are created using the _____ Tool Palette.

    A. Massing
    B. Concept
    C. General Drafting
    D. Documentation

13. Wall Styles are created by:

    A. Highlighting a Wall on the Wall tab of the Tool Palette, right click and select Wall Styles
    B. Type **WallStyle** on the command line
    C. Go to **Format→Style Manager**
    D. All of the above

14. To create a New Layer, use:

    A. Type **LayerManager** at the command line
    B. Type **Layer** at the command line
    C. Use **Format→Layer Management→Layer Manager**
    D. All of the above

15. You can change the way AEC objects are displayed by using:

    A. Edit Object Display
    B. Edit Display Properties
    C. Edit Entity Properties
    D. Edit AEC Properties

ANSWERS:

1) T; 2) T; 3) T; 4) F; 5) T; 6) T; 7) T; 8) T; 9) A; 10) A; 11) A; 12) A; 13) D; 14) D; 15) A

Lesson 3
Floor Plans

The floor plan is central to any architectural drawing. In the first exercise, we convert an AutoCAD 2D floor plan to 3D. In the remaining exercises, we work in 3D.

Exercise 3-1:
Going from a 2D to 3D Floor plan

Drawing Name: New
Estimated Time: 45 minutes

This exercise reinforces the following skills:

- ❏ Create Walls
- ❏ Wall Properties
- ❏ Wall Styles
- ❏ Style Manager
- ❏ Insert an AutoCAD drawing
- ❏ Trim, Fillet, Extend Walls

1. Start a new drawing using QNEW or select the + tab.

2. Type **UNITS** on the command line.

Set the Units to **Inches**.
Set the Type to **Architectural**.
Set the Precision to **0′ 1/8″**.

Press **OK**.

3.　

Activate the **Insert** ribbon.

Select **Attach**.

4.

Locate the *autocad_floor_plan.dwg* file in the exercises. *Set your Files of type to Drawing (*.dwg) to locate the file.* Press **Open**.

5.

Uncheck Insertion Point.
Uncheck Scale.
Uncheck Rotation.
This sets everything to the default values.

Press **OK**.

6.

Use the ViewCube to switch to a 3D view.

Note that the AutoCAD file is 2D only.

Return to a top view.

7.

Select the attached xref.
Right click and select
Bind→Insert.
This converts the xref to an inserted block.

8.　Select the block reference and type **EXPLODE** to convert to lines.

9. Activate the **Home** ribbon.

   Select the **Measure** tool on the Inquiry panel.

10. Measure a wall thickness.

    Note that the walls are 1'-11" thick.

    1'-11"

    Endpoint

11. Launch the **Design Tools** palette from the Home ribbon.

12. Set the tool palette to display all palettes and activate the Walls palette.

13.

Locate the Stud-4 Rigid-1.5 Air-1 Brick-4 wall style. Right click and select **Import Stud-4 Rigid-1.5 Air-1 Brick-4 Wall Style**.

This adds the wall style to the active drawing.

14.

Locate the Stud-4 Rigid-1.5 Air-1 Brick-4 wall style.
Right click and select **Wall Styles**.

This launches the Style Manager.

15.
```
Drawing10.dwg
  Architectural Objects
    Wall Styles
      Brick_Block
      Standard
      Stud-3.5 Rigid-1.5 Air-1 Brick-4
```

Note that the only wall styles available are Standard, Brick_Block (which was added to the template) and the style that was just imported.

Highlight the **Stud-4 Rigid-1.5 Air-1 Brick-4** wall style.

16. Total Width: 11 1/8"

Note the components listed in the Style Manager for the wall style. The total wall thickness is 11-1/8".

We need a wall style that is 1'–11". We need to add 11- 7/8" of material to the wall style.

17. Select the **Add Component** tool.

18.

Index	Name	Priority	Width	Edge Offset	Function	Dimens
1	Brick Ven...	810	4"	2 1/2"	Non-Struct...	☑
2	Air Gap	700	1"	1 1/2"	--	☐
3	Rigid Insul...	600	1 1/2"	0"	Non-Struct...	☐
4	Stud	500	3 1/2"	-3 1/2"	Structural	☑
5	GWB	1200	5/8"	-4 1/8"	Non-Struct...	☐
6	GWB	1200	5/8"	-4 3/4"	Non-Struct...	☐

Position another 5/8" piece of GWB (gypsum board) so it is on the interior side.

19. Select the **Add Component** tool.

20.

Total Width: 1'-11"

Index	Name	Priority	Width	Edge Offset	Function	Dimension			Bottom Elevation Offset
1	Brick Ven...	810	4"	2 1/2"	Non-Structural	☑	☐	☐	0"
2	CMU	700	1'-3 7/8"	2 1/2"	--	☐	☐	☐	0"
3	Air Gap	700	1"	1 1/2"	--	☐	☐	☐	0"
4	Rigid Insul...	600	1 1/2"	0"	Non-Structural	☐	☐	☐	0"
5	Stud	500	4"	-4"	Structural	☑	☐	☑	0"
6	GWB	1200	5/8"	-4"	Non-Structural	☐	☐	☑	0"
7	GWB	1200	5/8"	-4 5/8"	Non-Structural	☐	☐	☑	0"

Add a layer called CMU that is 1' 3.875" thick.

Position the CMU so it is behind the brick veneer.

21. Verify that your layers are set as shown. Verify that the total width is 1' 11".

22. Press **OK** to close the Styles Manager dialog.

23. Locate the **Stud-4 Rigid-1.5 Air-1 Brick-4** wall style on the Walls tab of the Design Palette.

24. Right click on the wall style and select **Properties**.

25. Under Dimensions:
Set Justify to **Left** using the drop-down.
Press **OK**.
This sets the location line for the wall.

26. Right click on the **Stud-4 Rigid-1.5 Air-1 Brick-4** wall style and select **Apply Tool Properties to → Linework**.

27. Select the outside segments of the walls.

Do not select any of the interior walls.

Press ENTER when you are done selecting lines.

28. You will be prompted if you want to erase any of the linework. Enter **NO**.

29.

Zoom into one of the walls that was placed.

Note that it is the correct width. The blue arrow indicates the exterior side of the wall. If the blue arrow is inside the building, click on the blue arrow and it will flip the orientation of the wall.

If necessary, move walls so they are aligned with the floor plan's walls.

30.

Switch to a 3D view.

You should see 3D walls where you selected lines.

31.

To join the walls together, use FILLET with an R value of 0.
Type FILLET, then select the two walls to be joined to form a corner.

32.

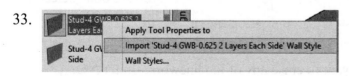

In the plan view, the exterior walls should form a closed figure.

33.

Stud-4 GWB-0.625 2 Layers Ea
Apply Tool Properties to
Stud-4 GV   Import 'Stud-4 GWB-0.625 2 Layers Each Side' Wall Style
Side   Wall Styles...

Locate the **Stud-4 GWB-0.625-2 Layers Each Side** wall style. Right click and select **Import Stud-4 GWB-0.625-2 Layers Each Side Wall Style**.

34. Locate the **Stud-4 GWB-0.625-2 Layers Each Side** Wall Style.

Right click and select Wall Styles.
This will launch the Styles Manager.

35. Highlight the **Stud-4 GWB-0.625-2 Layers Each Side** Wall Style.

Select the Components tab.

The total width for this wall style is 6 1/2"

36. Change the Stud width to **1' 9 3/4"**.

Adjust the positions of the components so that the wall looks proper.

Press **OK** to close the Style Manager.

37. 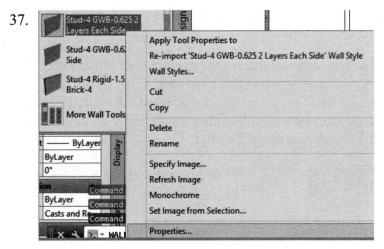 Switch to a Top view of the floor plan.

Select the **Stud-4 GWB-0.625-2 Layers Each Side** Wall Style.

Right click on the wall style and select **Properties**.

38.

Under Dimensions:
Set Justify to **Left** using the drop-down.
Press **OK**.
This sets the location line for the wall.

39. Select the **Stud-4 GWB-0.625-2 Layers Each Side** wall style.

Right click and select **Apply Tool Properties to → Linework**.

40.

Select the inside segments of the walls.

Do not select any of the exterior walls.

Press ENTER when you are done selecting lines.

41. You will be prompted if you want to erase any of the line work. Enter **NO**.

42.

Zoom into one of the walls that was placed. Note that it is the correct width.

The blue arrow indicates the exterior side of the wall. If the blue arrow is inside the building, click on the blue arrow and it will flip the orientation of the wall. Because these are interior walls with gypsum board on both sides, the orientation doesn't matter.

If necessary, move walls so they are aligned with the floor plan's walls.

43.

Use the TRIM, EXTEND, and FILLET tools to edit the interior walls.

44.

Some of your walls may display a warning symbol.

This means that you have walls overlapping each other.

Check to see if you have more than one wall or if you need to trim the walls.

45. Save as *ex3-1.dwg*.

The ex3-1 file can be downloaded from the publisher's website, so you can check your file against mine and see how you did.

Exercise 3-2:

Creating Walls

Drawing Name: New
Estimated Time: 10 minutes

This exercise reinforces the following skills:

- ❑ Create Walls
- ❑ Wall Properties
- ❑ Wall Styles
- ❑ Model and Work space

1. Start a new drawing using QNEW.

2. Select the **Wall** tool from the Home ribbon.

3. In the Properties dialog, check under the Style drop-down list.

Only the Brick_Block and Standard styles are available.

These are the wall styles that are loaded in the template.

4. Exit out of the command by pressing ESC.

5. Launch the Design Tools palette from the Home ribbon.

6. Right click on the left bar of the palette and enable **All Palettes**.

7. Select the Walls palette.

8. Activate the Walls tab on the palette.
Select the CMU-8 Rigid-1.5 Air 2 Brick-4

[CMU 190 Rigid-038 Air – 050 Brick -090].

9. Toggle **ORTHO** ON.

Start the wall at 0,0.
Create a rectangle 72 inches [1830 mm] tall and 36 inches [914 mm] wide.

You can use Close to close the rectangle.

Place the walls as if you are drawing lines.

10. Go to the **View** ribbon.

11. Toggle on the Layout tabs.

12. Select the **Work** tab now visible in the lower left corner of the screen.

13.

The work tab opens up a layout with two viewports. One viewport is 3D and the other viewport is a top view.

You see that the walls you placed are really 3-dimensional.

14.

Switch back to the Model space tab.

15.

Select the **Wall** tool from the Home ribbon.

16.

Style	Standard
Bound spaces	Brick_Block
Cleanup automatically	CMU-8 Rigid-1.5 Air-2 Brick-4
Cleanup group definition	Standard
Segment type	Line

Browse...

In the Properties dialog, check under the Style drop-down list.

Note that the CMU wall style is now available under the drop-down list.

17. Exit out of the command by pressing ESC.

18. Save your drawing as *Ex3-2.dwg*.

Tips & Tricks

➢ If you draw a wall and the materials composing the wall are on the wrong side, you can reverse the direction of the wall. Simply select the wall, right click and select the Reverse option from the menu.

➢ To add a wall style to a drawing, you can import it or simply create the wall using the Design Tools.

➢ Many architects use external drawing references to organize their projects. That way, teams of architects can concentrate just on their portions of a building. External references also use less system resources.

> ➤ You can convert lines, arcs, circles, or polylines to walls. If you have created a floor plan in AutoCAD and want to convert it to 3D, open the floor plan drawing inside of AutoCAD Architecture. Use the Convert to Walls tool to transform your floor plan into walls.

> ➤ To create a freestanding door, press the ENTER key when prompted to pick a wall. You can then use the grips on the door entity to move and place the door wherever you like.

> ➤ To move a door along a wall, use Door→Reposition→Along Wall. Use the OSNAP From option to locate a door a specific distance from an adjoining wall.

Exercise 3-3:

Creating a Floor Plan using an Image

Drawing Name: new.dwg
Estimated Time: 60 minutes

This exercise reinforces the following skills:

- ❑ Insert Image
- ❑ Add Wall

1.   Start a new drawing using QNEW or use the + tab.

2.   Select the **Insert** ribbon.

Select the **Attach** tool.

3.   Browse to the folder where the exercises are stored.

Change the Files of type to **All image files**.

4.   Select the *floorplan1* file.

Press **Open**.

5.

Uncheck the insertion point to insert the image at **0, 0, 0**.

Set the Scale to **113.00**.
Set the Angle to **0.0**.

Press **OK**.

6.   To prevent your image from moving around:

Create a new layer called image.
Select the image.
Right click and select Properties.
Assign the image to the image layer.
Lock the image layer.

7. Open the Design Tools palette.
Launch All Palettes.
Select the Walls palette.

8. Locate the **Stud-4 Rigid 1.5 Air-1 Brick-4** wall style.

9. Draw a wall on the far left side of the floor plan, tracing over the wall shown in the image file.

Orient the wall so the exterior side of the wall is on the outside of the building.

10. Offset the wall 15′ 11-1/8″ to the right.

The additional offset takes into account the wall thickness of 11-1/8″.

Flip the wall orientation so the wall exterior is on the outside of the building.

Check the offset distance to ensure the two walls are 15′ apart from inside finish face to inside finish face.

11. Trace a horizontal wall using the **Stud-4 Rigid 1.5 Air-1 Brick-4** wall style.

12.
Offset the horizontal wall 12' 4.625".
This is 11' 5 1/2" plus 11 1/8".

Verify that the distance from finish face to finish face is 11' 5 ½".

13. Locate the **Stud-4 GWB-0.625 Each Side** wall style on the Design Tools palette.

14. Right click and select **Apply Tool Properties to → Wall**.

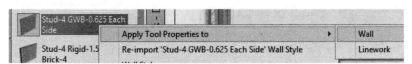

15. Select the upper horizontal wall.

Press **ENTER**.

16. The wall style will update.

17. Place a **Stud-4 Rigid 1.5 Air-1 Brick-4** wall at the top horizontal location of the Master Bedroom.

Verify that the orientation is for the exterior side of the wall outside the building.

18. Use the FILLET command to create corners between the vertical and horizontal walls.

Type FILLET and select the horizontal wall, then select a vertical wall. Repeat for the other side.

19. Offset the top horizontal wall 16′ 10.625″.

20. Locate the **Stud-4 GWB-0.625 Each Side** wall style on the Design Tools palette.

21. Right click and select **Apply Tool Properties to → Wall**.

22.

    Select the lower horizontal wall.

    Press **ENTER**.

23.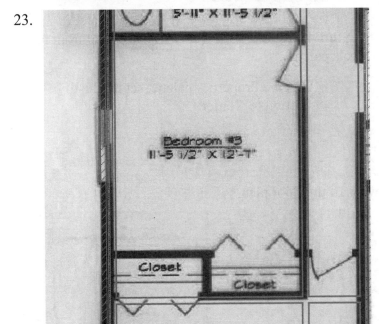

    Offset the left vertical exterior wall **12′ 4.625″**.

    Change the offset wall to the interior **Stud-4 GWB-0.625 Each Side** wall style using the **Apply Tool Properties to → Wall**.

24.

    Use an offset of 2′ 10″ to create the closet space.

25.

Adjust the position of the walls as needed to ensure they match the floor plan image.

26. Select the **Stud-4 Rigid 1.5 Air-1 Brick-4** wall tool from the Design Tools palette.

27.

Dimensions		
A	Width	1'-3 1/2"
B	Base height	10'-0"
C	Length	1"
	Justify	Center
*	Offset	0"
*F	Roof line offset from ba...	0"

On the Properties palette, set the Justify option to **Center**.

28. Trace the remaining south walls of the floor plan.

29.

Use the flip arrows to orient the exterior side of the walls to the outside of the building.

30.

Offset the left garage wall 21′ 3″.

Verify that the dimension from face to face of the interior side of the walls is 19′ 11 ½″.

31.

Offset the south garage wall 20′ 8″.

32.

Select the north garage wall.

In the Properties palette:
Change the wall style to **Stud-2.5 GWB-0.625 Each Side**.

33.

Adjust the position of the garage walls so the distance from interior face to interior face north-south is 20′ 8″ and the distance from interior face to interior face west-east is 19′ 11½″.

34.

Offset the south utility room wall up 8′ ¼″.

Verify that the distance from interior face to interior face is 7′ 7″.

35.

Offset the north utility wall 23′ 9.1325″.

Assign the top wall to the **Stud-4 Rigid 1.5 Air-1 Brick-4** wall style.

Verify that the distance from interior face to interior face is 23′ 3½″.

36.

Use the FILLET command to create the north east corner of the building.

37.

Place the west family room wall.

Verify that the distance from interior face to interior face is 20' 0".

38.

Trace over the floor plan to place the walls for the covered porch.

39.

Draw a line at a 45° angle to designate the wall for the kitchen.

40. Locate the **Stud-3.5 Rigid 1.5 Air-1 Brick-4 Wall** style.
Right click and **Apply Tool Properties to → Linework** and select the angled line.

41. Use the BREAK tool to divide the walls that need to be split into the two different styles.

42. The walls indicated should be broken using the BREAK tool so one segment can remain exterior and one segment can be changed to the interior wall style.

43.

Change the interior wall segments to the interior wall style.

44.

Use the EXTEND tool to extend the interior walls.

A triangle symbol with an exclamation point indicates that you have a wall interference condition – usually a wall on top of a wall.

45.

Select the interior wall with the interference condition.

Right click and select **Cleanups → Add Wall Merge Condition**.

46.

Select the two exterior walls where it is interfering.

The walls will merge and clean up the intersection area.

47.

Zoom into the area near the utility room and notice some of the walls may need to be cleaned up as well.

48.

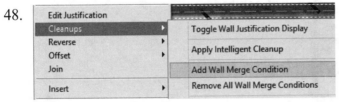

Select one of the interior walls. Right click and select **Cleanups → Add Wall Merge Condition**.

49.

Select both walls.

The wall intersection cleans up.

50.

Repeat for the south utility wall.

51.

Zoom into the Bedroom #2 area.

Use FILLET to eliminate the extra interior walls. Select the walls at the locations indicated to clean up the room.

52.

Offset the south bathroom wall 6′ 4.25″.

Verify that the distance from interior face to interior face is 5′ 11″.

53.

Add the interior walls for the lavatory areas.

Use the wall style: **Stud-4 GWB-0.625 Each Side**.

54.

Unlock the image layer.

Select the image.
Right click and select Image→Adjust.

55. You can adjust how much of the image you see so it doesn't interfere with your work.

Alternatively, you can freeze the image layer or change the transparency of the layer.

56.

You should have a completed floor plan.

Save as *ex3-3.dwg*.

Exercise 3-4:

Adding Doors

Drawing Name: Ex3-3.dwg
Estimated Time: 45 minutes

This exercise reinforces the following skills:

- ❑ Adding Doors
- ❑ Door Properties

1. Open *ex3-3.dwg*.

2. Thaw the image layer so you can see where doors are located if you froze that layer or adjust the image so you can see the door locations.

3. Open the Design Tools palette.

4. Bifold - Double   Locate the **Bifold-Double** door on the Doors tab on the Tools palette.

5. Highlight the **Bifold - Double** door.
Right click and select **Properties**.

6. Expand the **Dimensions** section.
Set the size to:
4'-6" x 6'-8".

Set the Opening percent to **50**.

If you left click in the Standard sizes field, a down arrow will appear...select the down arrow and you will get a list of standard sizes. Then, select the size you want.

A 25% opening will show a door swing at a 45-degree angle.
The value of the Opening percentage determines the angle of the arc swing.
A 50% value indicates the door will appear half-open at a 90-degree angle.

7. [Location table image] Expand the **Location** section.

Set Position along wall to **Offset/Center**.
This will allow the user to snap to the center position along the wall.

Press **OK** to close the Properties dialog.

8. Place the Bifold - Double doors at the two closets.

The orientation of the door swing is determined by the wall side selected.

In both cases, you want to select the outside face of the wall. Center the closet door on each wall.

9.

Place the **Bifold - Double** door at each of the closets located in Bedroom #2 and Bedroom #3.

10.

Place the **Bifold - Double** door at the closet next to the entry way.

The exclamation mark indicates that the door is too wide for the wall.

11.

Select the door.

In the Properties palette:
Change the width of the Bifold - Double door to **4' 0"**.

The door updates and the warning symbol disappears.

The door now fits.

12. Bifold - Single   Locate the **Bifold - Single** door on the Doors tab of the Design Tools palette.

13.

In the Properties palette:

Set the door to use the Standard Size
2′ 4″ x 6′ 8″.
Set the Opening percent to **50**.
Press **OK** to close the Properties palette.

14.

Place the door in the Linen Closet near the lavatories.

15. Hinged - Single - Exterior

Locate the **Hinged - Single - Exterior** door on the Doors tab of the Design Tools palette.

16.

A	Width	3′-0″
B	Height	6′-8″
	Measure to	--
	Swing angle	30

In the Properties palette:

Set the door to use the size
3′ 0″ x 6′ 8″.
Set the Swing angle to **30**.

17.

Select the side of the wall that will be used for the door swing and place the entry door.

18. Hinged - Single

Locate the **Hinged - Single** door on the Doors tab of the Design Tools palette.

19.

A	Width	2′-6″
B	Height	6′-8″
	Measure to	--
	Swing angle	30

In the Properties palette:

Set the door to use the size:
2′ 6″ x 6′ 8″.
Set the Swing angle to **30**.

20.

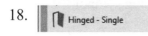

*	Relative to grid	--
*	Position along wall	Offset/Center
*	Automatic offset	4 7/8″
*	Justification	--
	Vertical alignment	--

Set the Position along wall to **Offset/Center**.

21.

Place the door in Bedroom #2.

22.

Place the door in Bedroom #3.

The swing is on the correct side, but not the correct direction.

23.

Select the door so it highlights.

The horizontal arrow flips the orientation of the door to the other side of the wall.

The vertical arrow flips the orientation of the door swing.

Left click on the vertical arrow.

The door updates to match the floor plan image.

24.

Place a **Hinged - Single** door in Bath #2.

25. Place a **Hinged - Single** door in the Utility Room.

Set the swing angle to **70**.

26. | Hinged - Single - Exterior | Locate the **Hinged - Single - Exterior** door on the Doors tab of the Design Tools palette.

27.

Dimensions		
	Standard sizes	2'-6" X 6'-8"
A	Width	2'-6"
B	Height	6'-8"
	Measure to	Inside of frame
	Swing angle	30

In the Properties palette:

Set the door to use the Standard Size **2′ 6″ x 6′ 8″**.
Set the Swing angle to **30**.

28. Place the door between the Utility Room and the Garage.

29. Place the door on the east wall of the Utility Room.

30. | Overhead - Sectional | Locate the **Overhead - Sectional** door on the Doors tab of the Design Tools palette.

31.

Dimensions		
	Bound spaces	By style (Yes)
	Standard sizes	16'-0" X 6'-8" (Custo...
A	Width	16'-0"
B	Height	6'-8"
	Measure to	Inside of frame
	Opening percent	0

In the Properties palette:

Set the door to use the Standard Size **16′ 0″ x 6′ 8″**.
Set the Opening percent to **0**.

32. Place the garage door.

33. Sliding - Double - Full Lite   Locate the **Sliding - Double - Full Lite** door on the Doors tab of the Design Tools palette.

34.

Dimensions	
Standard sizes	--
A Width	5'-4"
B Height	6'-8"
Measure to	--
Opening per...	0

In the Properties palette:

Set the door to use the Standard Size **5′ 4″ x 6′ 8″**.
Set the Opening percent to **0**.

35. Place the door in the family room.

36.

Place a second **Sliding - Double - Full Lite** door on the east wall of the Master Bedroom.

37.

Standard sizes	10'-0" X 6'-8" (Custo...	
A Width	10'-0"	
B Height	6'-8"	
Measure to	Inside of frame	
Opening percent	50	

Set the door to use the size: **10′ 0″ x 6′ 8″**.
Set the Opening Percent to **50**.

38.

Center the door on the north wall of the Living Room.

39. Pocket - Single

Locate the **Pocket - Single** door on the Doors tab of the Design Tools palette.

40.

Dimensions		
Standard sizes	--	
A Width	2'-6"	
B Height	6'-8"	
Measure to	--	
Opening per...	50	

In the Properties palette:

Set the door to use the size: **2′ 6″ x 6′ 8″**.
Set the Opening percent to **50**.

41.

Place the door in the lower right corner of the Master Bedroom.

42.

In the Properties palette:

Set the door to use the Standard Size **2′ 4″ x 6′ 8″**.
Set the Opening percent to **50**.

43.

Center the pocket door on the lower horizontal wall between the Master Bedroom closets.

44.

Image layer is adjusted to be faded. Dimensions were moved to a layer named A-Anno-Dim and then frozen.

This is the floor plan so far.

45. Save as *ex3-4.dwg*.

Switch to an isometric view and you will see that your model is 3D.

Look at the model using different visual styles. Which style do you like best? The model shown uses a Shaded visual style as defined by the dialog shown.

Exercise 3-5:
Create an Arched Opening Tool

Drawing Name: ex3-4.dwg
Estimated Time: 10 minutes

This exercise reinforces the following skills:

- ❑ Copying Tools
- ❑ Tool Properties

1.   Open *ex3-4.dwg*.

2.   ⌐ Cased Opening   Locate the **Cased Opening** tool on the Doors palette.

3. 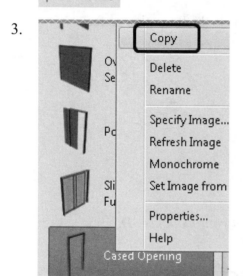   Right click and select **Copy**.

4.   Select the **Doors** tab.
    Right click and select **Paste**.

5. 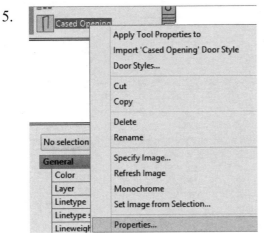 *The copied tool is located at the bottom of the palette.*

Highlight the copied tool.
Right click and select **Properties**.

6. 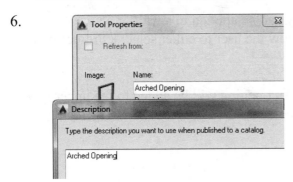 Change the Name to **Arched Opening**.
Change the Description to **Arched Opening**.
Press **OK**.

7. Expand the General section.
Set the Description to **Creates an Arched Opening**.
Press **OK**.

8. 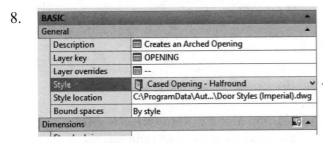 Set the Layer key to **OPENING**.
Set the Style to **Cased Opening-Half round**.

Press **OK**.

 The tool is defined in the palette.

9. Save as *ex3-5.dwg*.

Exercise 3-6:
Adding an Opening

Drawing Name: ex3-5.dwg
Estimated Time: 15 minutes

This exercise reinforces the following skills:

- Adding Openings
- Opening Properties
- Copying Tools
- Set Image from Selection

Openings can be any size and elevation. They can be applied to a wall or be freestanding. The Add Opening Properties allow the user to either select a Pre-defined shape for the opening or use a custom shape.

An opening will be added to the upper wall between the Master Bedroom closets.

1.   Open *ex3-5.dwg*.

2.   **Arched Opening**   Select the **Arched Opening** tool.

3.

Dimensions	
Standard sizes	2'-6" X 6'-8" (Custom...
A Width	2'-6"
B Height	6'-8"
Measure to	Inside of frame
Opening percent	0

In the Properties palette:

Set the door to use the size:
2′ 6″ x 6′ 8″.

4.

Location	
✳ Relative to grid	No
✳ Position along wall	Offset/Center
✳ Automatic offset	6"
✳ Justification	Center

Expand the Location section in the Properties palette.
Set the Position along wall to **Offset/Center**.
Set the Automatic offset to **6″ [300.00]**.

5.

Place the arched opening in the wall between the closets in the Master Bedroom. Center it on the wall.

6.

Dimensions	
Standard sizes	3'-0" X 6'-8"
A Width	3'-0"
B Height	6'-8"
Measure to	Inside of frame
Opening percent	50

In the Properties palette:

Set the door to use the size:
3' 0" x 6' 8".

7.

Place the Arched Opening on the left side of the Foyer above the Entry.

8. Use the View tools on the View ribbon **View → NE Isometric** and **3D orbit** to view the arched opening.

9. On the View ribbon:

Switch to a **Shades of Gray** display.

If your walls are reversed, you can change the orientation in the plan/top view.

10. Set the **Materials/Textures On**.

Materials / Textures Off

Materials On / Textures Off

Materials / Textures On

11. Set to **Full Shadows**.

Note how the display changes.

No Shadows

Ground Shadows

Full Shadows

When materials, textures, and shadows are enabled, more memory resources are used.

12. 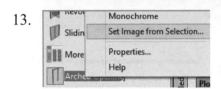 Locate the Arched Opening placed in the Master Bedroom.

13.   Select the **Arched Opening** icon on the tool palette. Right click and select **Set Image from Selection...** Pick the arched opening you created. Press **Enter**.

A dialog box allows you to choose which object to use for the image selection.

 If you have Selection Cycling enabled, you will see a selection dialog box.

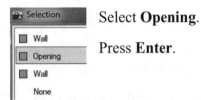 Select **Opening**.

Press **Enter**.

You can select more than one object for your image selection.

The tool icon updates with the new image.

14. Select the Work tab to view your model.

15. Save the file as *ex3-6.dwg*.

Exercise 3-7
Add Window Assemblies

Drawing Name: ex3-6.dwg
Estimated Time: 30 minutes

This exercise reinforces the following skills:

❑   Add Windows

1.   Open ex3-6.*dwg*.

Switch to a Top View.

2.   Activate the **Design Tools** from the Home ribbon, if they are not launched.

3.   Select the Windows tab of the Tool palette.

4.   Picture   Select the **Picture** window.

5.   Expand the Dimensions section.
Set the size to **6'-0" x 5'-0"**.

6.
Expand the Location section.
Set the Position to **Offset/Center**.
Set the Automatic Offset to **6″**.

7.
Select the midpoint of the north Master Bedroom wall.

8.
On the Properties palette:

Expand the Dimensions section.
Change the Width to **9′-0″**.
Change the Height to **4′-0″**.

9.
Place the window at the midpoint of the south wall in the Dining Area.

10.
On the Properties palette:

Expand the Dimensions section.
Change the Width to **12′-10″**
Change the Height to **4′-0″**.

11. Place the window at the midpoint of the north wall for the Family Room.

12. Select the **Casement - Double** window on the Windows palette.

13.

Dimensions		
Standard sizes	4'-0" X 4'-0" (Custom...	
A Width	4'-0"	
B Height	4'-0"	
Measure to	Outside of frame	
Swing angle	0	

On the Properties palette:

Expand the Dimensions section.
Change the Width to **4'-0"**.
Change the Height to **4'-0"**.

14. Place the window in the west wall of Bedroom #2.

15. Place the window in the west wall of Bedroom #3.

16. Select the **Casement** window.

17.

Bound spaces	By style (Yes)	
Dimensions		
Standard sizes	2'-0" X 4'-0" (Custom...	
A Width	2'-0"	
B Height	4'-0"	
Measure to	Outside of frame	
Swing angle	0	

On the Properties palette:

Expand the Dimensions section.
Change the Width to **2'-0"** .
Change the Height to **4'-0"**.

18.

Place two windows on the west wall of the bathrooms.

19.

Place two windows on the east wall of the Family Room.

20.

Dimensions		
Standard sizes	3'-0" X 4'-0" (Custom...	
A Width	3'-0"	
B Height	4'-0"	
Measure to	Outside of frame	

On the Properties palette:

Expand the Dimensions section.
Change the Width to **3'-0"** .
Change the Height to **4'-0"**.

21.

Place the window in the south wall of the Garage.

22. Save as *ex3-7.dwg*.

Notes:

Lesson 4
Space Planning

A residential structure is divided into three basic areas:

- ❑ Bedrooms: Used for Sleeping and Privacy
- ❑ Common Areas: Used for gathering and entertainment, such as family rooms, living rooms, and dining area
- ❑ Service Areas: Used to perform functions, such as the kitchen, laundry room, garage, and storage areas

When drawing your floor plan, you need to verify that enough space is provided to allow placement of items, such as beds, tables, entertainment equipment, cars, stoves, bathtubs, lavatories, etc.

AutoCAD Architecture comes with Design Content to allow designers to place furniture to test their space.

Exercise 4-1:
Creating AEC Content

Drawing Name: new
Estimated Time: 20 minutes

This lesson reinforces the following skills:

- ❑ Design Center
- ❑ AEC Content
- ❑ Customization

1.   Start a new drawing using **QNEW** or press the + tab.

2.   Activate the Insert ribbon.

    Select **Attach**.

3.   Browse for *ex3-8.dwg* and press **Open**.

4.

Accept the defaults.

Uncheck **Specify On-screen** for the insertion point.

Press **OK**.

5.

Launch the XREF Manager by selecting the small arrow in the Reference drop-down.

6. The palette lists the file references now loaded in the drawing.
Notice that the floorplan image file is listed as a reference.

7.

Zoom Extents.

You can do this by typing Z,E on the command line or using the tool on the View ribbon.

8.

Launch the Design Center from the Insert ribbon or press Ctrl+2.

9. Select the AEC Content tab.

Browse to *AutoCAD Architecture/Imperial/Design/ Furnishing/ Furniture/Bed*

10. Select the *Double.dwg* file.
Right click and select **Insert**.

11. Set Specify rotation to **Yes** in the Properties dialog.

12. Place the bed in Bedroom #2.

Right click and select ENTER to exit the command.

13. Locate the *Twin.dwg*.

14. Place the *Twin.dwg* in Bedroom#3.

Right click and select ENTER to exit the command.

15. Browse to the *Bedroom* folder in the *Metric/Design/Domestic Furniture* folder.

16. Locate the *3D 6 Drawer Chest*.

3D 6 Drawer Chest

17. Place a *3D 6 Drawer Chest* in the Bedroom #2. Right click and select ENTER to exit the command.

18. Add a 3D 3 Drawer Chest to Bedroom #3.

3D 3 Drawer Chest

19. Browse to the *Desk* folder under *AutoCAD Architecture/Imperial/Design/Furnishing/Furniture/.*

20.

36x18 Left

Locate the *36x18 Left.dwg* file under the *Desk* folder.
Place into Bedroom #2.

21. Locate the *6 Shelves.dwg* bookcase in the *Bookcase* folder.

22.

6 Shelves

Place in Bedroom #3.

23.

Switch to a 3D view and use 3D Orbit to view the furniture placement.

24. Save as *ex4-1.dwg*.

The Space Planning process is not just to ensure that the rooms can hold the necessary equipment, but also requires the drafter to think about plumbing, wiring, and HVAC requirements based on where and how items are placed.

As an additional exercise, place towel bars, soap dishes and other items in the bathrooms.

Exercise 4-2:
Furnishing the Common Areas

Drawing Name: Ex4-1.dwg
Estimated Time: 30 minutes

Common areas are the Living Room, Dining Room, and Family Room.

This lesson reinforces the following skills:

- Design Center
- Tool Palette
- Customization

You will need Internet access in order to complete this exercise. I have several blocks included to help you furnish your model. Feel free to explore and experiment with the different blocks.

1. Open *ex4-1.dwg*.

2. Launch the Design Center.

3. Launch the Tool Palette

4. 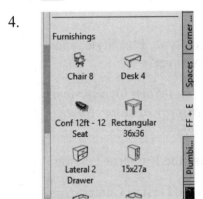 Activate the **FF + E tab** on the tool palette.
    Scroll down to the Furnishings area.

5. 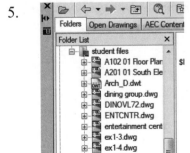 In the Design Center dialog, select the Folders tab.

    Browse to the folder where you stored the files downloaded from the publisher.

6. dining group.dwg Drag and drop the file called **dining group** onto the new palette.

7. Select the dining group tool.
    Right click and select **Properties**.

8. Change the name to **Dining Set**.

9. 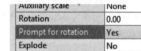 Set the Prompt for rotation to **Yes**.

10. 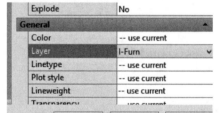 Set Layer **to I-Furn**.

    This ensures that the block will be placed on the I-Furn layer regardless of what layer is current.

11. Set the Color, Linetype, Plot Style, and Lineweight to ByLayer.

    This means that the I-Furn layer properties will control the display of color, linetype, plot style and lineweight.

    Press **OK** to close the Properties dialog.

12. Activate the **AEC Content** tab on the Design Center.

    Browse to *AutoCAD Architecture/Imperial/Design/Furnishing/Furniture/Chair* folder.

13. Drag and drop the **Lounge Circular** chair onto the Furniture palette.

14. Select the **Lounge Circular** tool.

Right click and select **Properties**.

15. 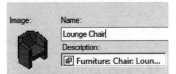 Change the name to **Lounge Chair**.

Press **OK** to close the Properties dialog.

16. Browse to *AutoCAD Architecture/Imperial/Design/Furnishing/Furniture/Sofa* folder.

Drag and drop the **Love Seat 2** onto the Furniture palette.

17. Select the **Love Seat 2** tool.
Right click and select **Properties**.

18. Change the Name to **Love Seat 6'**.

19. Browse to *AutoCAD Architecture/Imperial/Design/Furnishing/Furniture/Table* folder.

Drag and drop the **Coffee Table** onto the Furniture palette.

20. 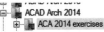 In the Design Center dialog, select the Folders tab.

Browse to the folder where you stored the files downloaded from the publisher.

21. Drag and drop the file called entertainment center onto the new palette.

22. Select the **entertainment center** tool. Right click and select **Properties**.

23. Change the name to **Entertainment Center**.

24. Set the Prompt for rotation to **Yes**.

25. Set Layer **to I-Furn**.

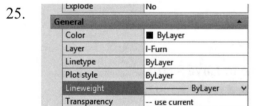

This ensures that the block will be placed on the I-Furn layer regardless of what layer is current. The available layers are in the active drawing.

26. Set the Color, Linetype, Plot Style, and Lineweight to ByLayer.

This means that the I-Furn layer properties will control the display of color, linetype, plot style and lineweight.

Press **OK** to close the Properties dialog.

27.

This is what your Furniture tool palette should look like.

There are additional furniture blocks in the student files you can add to the palette if you like.

28. Close the Design Center.

29.

Add the **Dining Set** to the dining room area by the kitchen.

30.

Furnish the living room.

31. Add a sofa and coffee table to the
    family room.

32. Save the file as *ex4-2.dwg*.

If the drawing preview in the Design Center is displayed as 2D, then it is a 2D drawing.

Exercise 4-3

Adding to the Service Areas

Drawing Name: Ex4-2.dwg
Estimated Time: 30 minutes

1. Open *ex4-2.dwg*.
   Select the Model tab.
   Switch to a top view.

2. Launch the Design Center.

3. 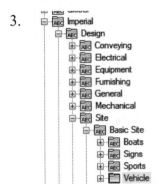 Select the AEC Content tab.
   Browse to the *AutoCAD Architecture/Imperial/Design/Site/ Basic Site/Vehicles* folder.

4. Drag and drop the *Sub-Compact* car into the garage.

Sub-Compact

All that remains are the kitchen and laundry areas.

5. Use the Design Center to add casework, a kitchen sink, and an oven into the kitchen area.

   There are also models available to you in the exercise files. The layout shown is the kitchen block included in the exercise files scaled to fit into the space.

6.   Our completed floor plan.

7.   Save the file as *ex4-4.dwg*.

QUIZ 2

True or False

1. Once a door or window is placed, it can not be moved or modified.

2. Openings can be any size and any elevation.

3. The Offset value when placing a door/window/opening determines how far the door/window/opening is placed from a selected point.

4. Door, window and opening dimensions can be applied using the Design Center.

Multiple Choice

5. Select the entity type that can NOT be converted to a wall:

    A. Line
    B. Polyline
    C. Circle
    D. Spline

6. A HOT grip is indicated by this color:

    A. GREEN
    B. BLUE
    C. RED
    D. YELLOW

7. To assign an image to a tool on the tool palette using existing geometry, use

    A. Assign image
    B. Set Image from selection
    C. Insert
    D. Import

ANSWERS:

1) F; 2) T 3) T; 4) F; 5) C; 6) C; 7) A

Notes:

Lesson 5
Roofs

Roofs can be created with single or double slopes, with or without gable ends, and with or without overhangs. Once you input all your roof settings, you simply pick the points around the perimeter of the building to define your roof outline. If you make an error, you can easily modify or redefine your roof.

You need to pick three points before the roof will begin to preview in your graphics window. There is no limit to the number of points to select to define the perimeter.

To create a gable roof, uncheck the gable box in the Roof dialog. Pick the two end points for the sloped portion of the roof. Turn on the Gable box. Pick the end point for the gable side. Turn off the Gable box. Pick the end point for the sloped side. Turn the Gable box on. Pick the viewport and then press ENTER. A Gable cannot be defined with more than three consecutive edges.

Roofs can be created using two methods: ROOFADD places a roof based on points selected or ROOFCONVERT which converts a closed polyline or closed walls to develop a roof.

> ➤ If you opt to use ROOFCONVERT and use existing closed walls, be sure that the walls are intersecting properly. If your walls are not properly cleaned up with each other, the roof conversion is unpredictable.
> ➤ The Plate Height of a roof should be set equal to the Wall Height.
> ➤ You can create a gable on a roof by gripping any ridgeline point and stretching it past the roof edge. You cannot make a gable into a hip using grips.

Shape – Select the Shape option on the command line by typing 'S.'	Single Slope – Extends a roof plane at an angle from the Plate Height.	end elevation view
	Double Slope – Includes a single slope and adds another slope, which begins at the intersection of the first slope and the height specified for the first slope.	end elevation view
Gable – Select the Gable option on the command line by typing 'G.'	If this is enabled, turns off the slope of the roof place. To create a gable edge, select Gable prior to identifying the first corner of the gable end. Turn off gable to continue to create the roof.	gable roof end
Plate Height – Set the Plate Height on the command line by typing 'PH.'	Specify the top plate from which the roof plane is projected. The height is relative to the XY plane with a Z coordinate of 0.	
Rise – Set the Rise on the command line by typing 'PR.'	Sets the angle of the roof based on a run value of 12.	A rise value of 5 creates a 5/12 roof, which forms a slope angle of 22.62 degrees.
Slope – Set the Slope on the command line by typing 'PS.'	Angle of the roof rise from the horizontal.	If slope angles are entered, then the rise will automatically be calculated.

Upper Height – Set the Upper Height on the command line by typing 'UH.'	This is only available if a Double Slope roof is being created. This is the height where the second slope will start.	
Rise (upper) – Set the Upper Rise on the command line by typing 'UR.'	This is only available if a Double Slope roof is being created. This is the slope angle for the second slope.	A rise value of 5 creates a 5/12 roof, which forms a slope angle of 22.62 degrees.
Slope (upper) – Set the Upper Slope on the command line by typing 'US.'	This is only available if a Double Slope roof is being created. Defines the slope angle for the second slope.	If an upper rise value is set, this is automatically calculated.
Overhang – To enable on the command line, type 'O.' To set the value of the Overhang, type 'V.'	If enabled, extends the roofline down from the plate height by the value set.	

	The Floating Viewer opens a viewer window displaying a preview of the roof.
	The match button allows you to select an existing roof to match its properties.
	The properties button opens the Roof Properties dialog.
	The Undo button allows you to undo the last roof operation. You can step back as many operations as you like up to the start.
	Opens the Roof Help file.

Exercise 5-1:

Creating a Roof using Existing Walls

Drawing Name: ex3-2.dwg
Estimated Time: 10 minutes

This exercise reinforces the following skills:

- ❏ Roof
- ❏ Roof Properties
- ❏ Visual Styles

1.   Open *ex3-2.dwg*.

2.   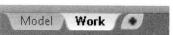

Select the Work icon. Activate the right viewport that shows the top or plan view.

3.   Select the **Roof** tool from the Home ribbon.

4.   Expand the Dimensions section.
Set the Thickness to **10″ [254.00 mm]**.
Set the Shape to **Single slope**.
Set the Overhang to **1′-0″ [609.6 mm]**.

Dimensions	
Thickness	254.00
Edge cut	Square
Shape	Single slope
Overhang	609.60
	Edges/Faces

5.   Expand the Lower Slope section.
Set the Plate height to **10′-0″ [3000 mm]**.

The plate height determines the level where the roof rests.

6.   Set the Rise to **1'-0" [100 mm]**.

7.   Pick the corners indicated to place the roof.

   Press **Enter**.

8. 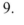 Activate the left 3D viewport.

9.   Activate the View ribbon.

   Select the **Shades of Gray** under Visual Styles.

10.   Save as *ex5-1.dwg*.

   Our roof works, but strictly speaking we can make it better with a couple of changes around the chimney. AutoCAD Architecture allows us to cut holes through roofs (to allow for vents, chimneys and skylights), and to add other faces or subsidiary roofs such as dormers.

   In order to edit a roof you have to convert it to Roof Slabs.

Exercise 5-2:

Roof Slabs

Drawing Name: ex3-8.dwg

Estimated Time: 15 minutes

This exercise reinforces the following skills:

- ❑   Convert to Roof
- ❑   Roof Slab Tools

1.   Open *ex3-8.dwg*.

2.   Select the **Roof** tool from the Home ribbon.

3.

Select the four corners on the left wing to place a roof.

4.

Repeat and select the four corners on the right wing to place a roof.

5.

Draw a rectangle around the middle section of the floor plan using the rectangle too.

6.

Select the rectangle.
Right click and select Properties.

7.

Change the elevation for the rectangle to 10'-0".

This puts it in-line with the top of the walls.

8.

Launch the Design Tools from the Home ribbon.

9.

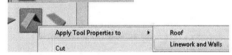

Locate the **Roof** tool on the Design palette. Right click and select **Apply Tool Properties to→Linework and Walls.**

10.

Select the rectangle.
Press ENTER to complete the selection.
When prompted to erase the linework, select **Yes**.
Press ENTER.
The middle roof is placed.

Press ESC to release any selection.

11.

Select the **Roof** on the left side.

The roof will highlight.

12.

Select **Convert** from the Roof ribbon.

13. Enable the **Erase layout geometry** checkbox.

Press **OK**.

The Roof Slab Properties dialog appears.
Close it.

14. The roof will change appearance slightly. It now consists of individual slabs.
Repeat for the other two roofs.

15.

Zoom into the area where the chimney is located.

Activate the Home ribbon.
Draw a rectangle over the outline of the chimney.
Make sure that the rectangle extends beyond the roof line.

16. Select the rectangle.

17.

Right click and select **Properties**.

Set the Elevation to **9′-6″ [3000]**.

This moves the rectangle to the same elevation as where the roof is placed.

Close the Properties dialog.
Deselect the rectangle by hitting the ESC key.

18. Select the roof slab located on top of the chimney.

Select **Hole→Add** from the ribbon.

19. At the next prompt pick the rectangle.
Press ENTER.

At the 'Erase Layout Geometry?' prompt hit, right click and select **Yes**.

The hole will appear.

Use the Viewcube in the viewport to orient the view so you can see the chimney.

The chimney now appears OK.

20. Save as *ex5-2.dwg*.

Exercise 5-3:
Modify Roof Line

Drawing Name: ex5-2.dwg
Estimated Time: 15 minutes

This exercise reinforces the following skills:

- ❑ Modify Roof Slabs
- ❑ Modify Roof Line

1. Open *ex5-2.dwg*.

2. Select the roof on the left wing.

3. Select the **Convert** tool on the ribbon.

4. Enable **Erase Layout Geometry**.
Press **OK**.

5. Erase the two roof slabs indicated.

6. Select the left roof slab.

7.

Drag the point at the bottom of the triangle up until it is horizontal to the upper point.

8.

Repeat for the right side.

9.

Repeat for the bottom side.

If you are having problems creating a straight edge, draw a horizontal line and snap to the line. Then, erase the line.

10.

Switch to a 3D view to see how the roof has changed.

View Style shown is 3D Hidden, Materials On, Realistic Face Style.

11.

Select the wall indicated.

12.

Select **Modify Roof Line** from the ribbon.

Roof/Floor Line

Edit in Place

Modify Roof Line

13. Type **A** for Autoproject.
     Select the two roof slabs.
     Press ENTER.

14.   The wall will auto-project to the roof.

     Press ESC to exit the command.

15.   Rotate the model so you can see the other side of the building.

16.   Select the wall indicated.

17. Select **Modify Roof Line** from the ribbon.

18. Type **A** for Autoproject.
     Select the two roof slabs.
     Press ENTER.

19. The wall will auto-project to the roof.

Press ESC to exit the command.

20. Save as *ex5-3.dwg*.

Exercise 5-4:

Trimming Roof Slabs

Drawing Name: ex5-3.dwg
Estimated Time: 30 minutes

This exercise reinforces the following skills:

- ❑ Roof Slabs
- ❑ Trim
- ❑ Grips

1. Open *ex5-3.dwg*.

2. Activate the **View** ribbon.

Select the **Top** view.

3. Delete the top triangle roof slab on the middle roof section.

4.

Place the top roof slab by selecting four points.

The arrows in the image indicate the points to left click to place the slab.
Right click and select Close to close the slab.

Press **ENTER** when all points are selected.

5.

Place the bottom roof slab using the four points indicated.
Right click and select Close to close the slab.

Press ENTER or CANCEL to exit the command.

6.

Edges	
Slope	
Rise	3 7/32"
Run	1'-0"
Slope	15.00

Select the top roof slab and set the Slope to **15**.

7.

Edges	
Slope	
Rise	3 7/32"
Run	1'-0"
Slope	15.00
Hold fascia ele...	No
Pivot Point X	-22'-9 1/4"

Select the bottom roof slab and set the Slope to **15**.

8. Switch to a **Left** view.

9. You can see how the slabs are positioned.

10. Switch to a SW Isometric view.

11. Select a roof slab.

12. Select **Trim** on the ribbon.

13.

Select the other roof slab to use as the trimming object.

Then select the edge of the roof to be trimmed.

The roof slab adjusts.

14.

Activate the NE Isometric view.

15.

Select the untrimmed roof slab.

16.

Select **Trim** on the ribbon.

17.

Select the other roof slab to use as the trimming object.

Then select the edge of the roof to be trimmed.

The roof slab adjusts.

18.

Select one of the roof slabs.

Use the grips to extend the slab into the adjoining roof slab.

19. Select the **Trim** tool on the ribbon.

Trim

20.

Select the adjoining roof slab to use as the trimming edge.

Then select the edge of the roof slab to be trimmed.

21. Repeat for the other side.

Orbit your model to see how well the roof slab is fitting.

22. Select the other roof slab.

23. Use the grips to extend the roof slab into the adjoining slab on each side.

Ortho: 9'-11 3/8" < 0.00°
Press Ctrl to cycle between:
- Move edge - maintain slope
- Move edge - change slope
- Add new edges - maintain slope
- Add new edges - change slope
- Convert to Arc - maintain slope
- Offset all edges - maintain slope

24. Select the TRIM tool on the ribbon.

25.

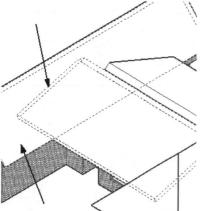

Select the roof slab to use as the trimming surface and the edge to be trimmed.

26.

Repeat for the other side of the roof slab.

27.

Save as *ex5-4.dwg*.

Exercise 5-5:
Roof Styles

Drawing Name: ex5-4.dwg
Estimated Time: 30 minutes

This exercise reinforces the following skills:

- ❏ Roof Styles
- ❏ Content Browser
- ❏ Design Palette

1.   Open *ex5-4.dwg*.

2.   Switch to an SW Isometric view.

3.   Launch the Design Tools.

4.   Right click on the Tool Palette and select **New Palette**.

5.   Rename the new palette – **Roofs**.

6. 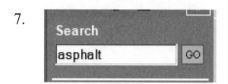 Launch the Content Browser.

7. 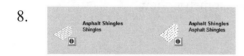 Type **asphalt** in the search field.
Press **GO**.

8. Drag and drop one of the asphalt shingles tools onto the palette.

9. Type **roof** in the search field.
Press **GO**.

10. Drag and drop the Plumb Cut Variable Thickness onto the palette.

11. Locate the rendering material for the Asphalt material.
Drag and drop it into the file.

12. Activate the Manage ribbon.

Select the **Style Manager**.

13. Locate the Roof Slab Styles under Architectural Objects.

Note that there is only one slab style available in the drawing.

14. Right click on the Roof Slab Style and select **New**.

15. Rename the style **Asphalt Shingles**.

16. Define three components:
- Asphalt Shingles with a thickness of ½" and Thickness Offset of 0.
- Membrane with a Thickness of 1/8" and Thickness offset of ½".
- Plywood Sheathing with a thickness of ¼" and Thickness offset of 5/8".

Use the preview to check the placement of each component.

17. Create new material definitions for the three new component types:

- Asphalt Shingles
- Membrane
- Plywood Sheathing

18. Highlight the Asphalt Shingles component.
Select **Edit Material Definition**.

19. Select the General Medium Detail style override.

Set the Hatch to use **AR-RSHKE**.

20.

Set the Angles to 0.

21.

Select the **Other** tab.
Under Surface Rendering:
Set the Render Material to the Asphalt Material that was placed in the file earlier.

Press **OK**.
Close the Style Manager.

22.

Switch to a top view.

23.

Select all the roof slabs.

24.

On the Properties palette:
Set the Style to **Asphalt Shingles**.

Press ESC to release the selection.

25.

Save as *ex5-5.dwg*.

Lesson 6
Structural Members

Architectural documentation for residential construction will always include plans (top views) of each floor of a building, showing features and structural information of the floor platform itself. Walls are located on the plan but not shown in structural detail.

Wall sections and details are used to show:

- the elements within walls (exterior siding, sheathing, block, brick or wood studs, insulation, air cavities, interior sheathing, trim)
- how walls relate to floors, ceilings, roofs, eaves
- openings within the walls (doors/windows with their associated sills and headers)
- how walls relate to openings in floors (stairs).

Stick-framed (stud) walls usually have their framing patterns determined by the carpenters on site. Once window and door openings are located on the plan, and stud spacing is specified by the designer (or the local building code), the specific arrangement of vertical members is usually left to the fabricators and not drafted, except where specific structural details require explanation.

The structural members in framed floors that have to hold themselves and/or other walls and floors up are usually drafted as framing plans. Designers must specify the size and spacing of joists or trusses, beams and columns. Plans show the orientation and relation of members, locate openings through the floor and show support information for openings and other specific conditions.

In the next exercises, we shall create a floor framing plan. Since the ground floor of our one-story lesson house has already been defined as a concrete slab, we'll assume that the ground level slopes down at the rear of the house and create a wood deck at the sliding door to the family room. The deck will need a railing for safety.

Autodesk AutoCAD Architecture includes a Structural Member Catalog that allows you to easily access industry-standard structural shapes. To create most standard column, brace, and beam styles, you can access the Structural Member Catalog, select a structural member shape, and create a style that contains the shape that you selected. The shape, similar to an AEC profile, is a 2D cross-section of a structural member. When you create a structural member with a style that you created from the Structural Member Catalog, you define the path to extrude the shape along.

You can create your own structural shapes that you can add to existing structural members, or use to create new structural members. The design rules in a structural member style allow you to add these custom shapes to a structural member, as well as create custom structural members from more than one shape.

All the columns, braces, and beams that you create are sub-types of a single Structural Member object type. The styles that you create for columns, braces, and beams have the same Structural Member Styles style type as well. When you change the display or style of a structural member, use the Structural Member object in the Display Manager and the Structural Member Styles style type in the Style Manager.

If you are operating with the AIA layering system as your current layer standard, when you create members or convert AutoCAD entities to structural members using the menu picks or toolbars, AutoCAD Architecture assigns the new members to layers: A-Cols, A-Cols-Brce or A-Beam, respectively. If Generic AutoCAD Architecture is your standard, the layers used are A_Columns, A_Beams and A_Braces. If your layer standard is Current Layer, new entities come in on the current layer, as in plain vanilla AutoCAD.

The Structural Member Catalog includes specifications for standard structural shapes. You can choose shapes from the Structural Member Catalog, and generate styles for structural members that you create in your drawings.

> A style that contains the catalog shape that you selected is created. You can view the style in the Style Manager, create a new structural member from the style, or apply the style to an existing member.

> When you add a structural member to your drawing, the shape inside the style that you created defines the shape of the member. You define the length, justification, roll or rise, and start and end offsets of the structural member when you draw it.

You cannot use the following special characters in your style names:

- less-than and greater-than symbols (< >)
- forward slashes and backslashes (/ \)
- quotation marks (")
- colons (:)
- semicolons (;)
- question marks (?)
- commas (,)
- asterisks (*)
- vertical bars (|)
- equal signs (=)
- backquotes (`)

The left pane of the Structural Member Catalog contains a hierarchical tree view. Several industry standard catalogs are organized in the tree, first by imperial or metric units, and then by material.

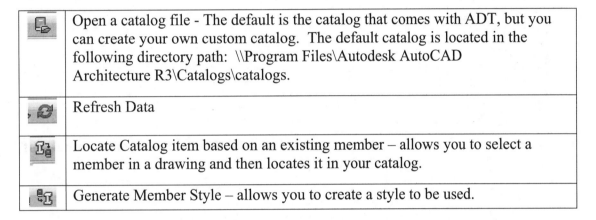

	Open a catalog file - The default is the catalog that comes with ADT, but you can create your own custom catalog. The default catalog is located in the following directory path: \\Program Files\Autodesk AutoCAD Architecture R3\Catalogs\catalogs.
	Refresh Data
	Locate Catalog item based on an existing member – allows you to select a member in a drawing and then locates it in your catalog.
	Generate Member Style – allows you to create a style to be used.

We will be adding a wood framed deck, 4000 mm x 2750 mm, to the back of the house. For purposes of this exercise we will assume that the ground level is 300 mm below the slab at the back of the house and falls away so that grade level below the edge of the deck away from the house is 2 meters below floor level: - 2 m a.f.f. (above finish floor) in architectural notation. We will place the top of the deck floorboards even with the top of the floor slab.

We will use support and rim joists as in standard wood floor framing, and they will all be at the same level, rather than joists crossing a support beam below. In practice this means the use of metal hangers, which will not be drawn. Once the floor system is drawn we will add support columns at the outside rim joist and braces at the columns.

Exercise 6-1:

Creating Member Styles

Drawing Name: ex5-4.dwg
Estimated Time: 5 minutes

This exercise reinforces the following skills:

- ❑   Creating Member Styles
- ❑   Use of Structural Members tools

1.   Open *ex5-4.dwg*

2.   Activate the Manage ribbon.

Go to **Style & Display → Structural Member Catalog**.

3.   Browse to the **Imperial/Timber/Lumber/Nominal Cut Lumber** folder.

4.   In the lower right pane:

Locate the **2x4** shape designation.

5.   Right click and select **Generate Member Style**.

6.   In the Structural Member Style dialog box, the name for your style automatically fills in.

Click **OK**.

7. In the lower right pane:

    Locate the **2x6** shape designation.
    Right click and select **Generate Member Style**.

8.
Structural Member Style	✕
New Name:	2x6
	OK Cancel

    In the Structural Member Style dialog box, the name for your style is displayed.

    Click **OK**.

9. Close the dialog.
    Save as *ex6-1.dwg*.

Exercise 6-2:
Creating Member Shapes

Drawing Name: ex6-1.dwg
Estimated Time: 10 minutes

This exercise reinforces the following skills:

❑ Structural Member Wizard

1. Open *ex6-1.dwg*.
    Select the Work tab.
    Activate the right viewport.

2.   Activate the **Manage** ribbon.

    Style   Display   Renovation
    Manager Manager   Mode

    Go to **Style & Display→Structural Member Wizard**.

    - Dimension Style Wizard
    - Profile Definitions
    - Member Shape
    - Insert as Polyline
    - Structural Member Catalog
    - Structural Member Wizard
    - Show Display Overrides
    - Style & Display

3.   Select the **Cut Lumber** category under Wood.

    Select Member Shape to create:
    - Concrete
    - Steel
    - Wood
      - Glue Laminated Beam
      - Cut Lumber
      - I Joist

    Press **Next**.

4.

Set the Section Width to **2″**.

Set the Section Depth to **10″**.

Press **Next**.

5.

Enter the style name as **2x10**.

Press **Finish**.

6.

Style Manager   Display Manager   Renovation Mode

Activate the **Manage** ribbon.

Go to **Style & Display → Structural Member Wizard**.

Dimension Style Wizard
Profile Definitions
Member Shape
Insert as Polyline
Structural Member Catalog
Structural Member Wizard
Show Display Overrides
Style & Display

7.

Select Member Shape to create:

Concrete
Steel
Wood
    Glue Laminated Beam
    Cut Lumber
    I Joist

Select the **Cut Lumber** category under Wood.

Press **Next**.

8.

Dimensions

Enter Dimensions for selected Member Shape:

Dimension	Value
A - Section Width	4″
B - Section Depth	4″

Set the Section Width to **4″**.

Set the Section Depth to **4″**.

Press **Next**.

9.

Enter the style name as **4x4**.

Press **Finish**.

Style Name

Enter style name:

4x4

Style Summary:

Shape Type
  Wood - Cut Lumber

Parameters
  A - Section Width : 4"
  B - Section Depth : 4"

10. Save as *ex6-2.dwg*.

Exercise 6-3:

Adding Structural Members

Drawing Name: ex6-2.dwg
Estimated Time: 25 minutes

This exercise reinforces the following skills:

- ❑ Creating Member Styles
- ❑ Use of Structural Members tools

1. Open *ex6-2.dwg*.

2. Activate the **Top** view.

Insert   Annotate   Render   **View**
  Top
  Bottom
  Left
  World
Appearance ▾   Coordina

3. Freeze the **A-Roof-Slab** layer.

A-Roof
A-Roof-Slab
A-Wall

This will make it easier to place the members for the pergola.

4. Thaw the **image** layer.

G-Anno-Stnd-Scrn
image   View
image

5. Activate the Tools palette if it is not available.

To activate, launch from the Home ribbon.

Tools
  Wall ▾
  Door ▾
  Window
Design Tools

6. Activate the **Design** palette.
To do this, right click on the palette and select **Design**.

If you do not see the Design palette, check to see which profile you have active. Set the current profile to AutoCAD Architecture (US Imperial).

We will place two columns at the locations indicated.

7. Column   Select the **Column** tool on the **Design** tool palette.

8. Set the Style to **4x4**.

Style	⬚ 4x4
Bound spaces	By style (No)
Trim automatically	By style (Yes)
✳ On object	Yes
Member type	▯ Column

9. Set the Justify value to **Middle Center**.
Set the Logical Length to **10′ -0″**.

Dimensions	
A Start offset	0"
B End offset	0"
C Logical length	10'-0"
✳ Specify roll on screen	Yes
E Roll	0.00
Justify	⊞ Middle Center
Justify cross-section	Maximum
Justify components	Highest priority only

10.

Place two columns at the locations indicated on the floor plan image.

11. On the View ribbon:
Switch to a **NE Isometric view**.

 You should see two columns in the porch area.

12. Switch back to a **Top** view.

You can use the Zoom Previous tool to return to the previous view.

13. Beam   Select the **Beam** tool from the Designs Palette.

14.

Style	2x4
Bound spaces	By style (No)
Trim automatically	By style (Yes)
On object	Yes
Member type	Beam
imensions	
Start offset	0"
End offset	0"
Logical length	1"
Roll	270.00
Layout type	Fill
Justify	Bottom Center
Justify cross-secti...	Maximum
Justify components	Highest priority only

Set the Style to **2x4**.

Set Justify to **Bottom Center**.

15. Select the node of the column as the start point and perpendicular point at the left wall as the end point.

16. Place a second beam from the center of the left column to the center of the right column.

17. Place a third beam starting at the node center of the column and perpendicular to the right wall.

18. Right click and select ENTER to exit the command.

19. Select all three beams.

20. On the Properties palette:

Location	▲
Start point X	*VARIES*
Start point Y	*VARIES*
Start point Z	10'-0"
End point X	*VARIES*
End point Y	*VARIES*
End point Z	10'-0"
Rotation	*VARIES*
Elevation	10'-0"
	Additional information

Set the Start point Z to **10′ 0″**.
Set the End point Z to **10′ 0″**.

Note the Elevation updates to 10′ 0″.

Press ESC to release the selection set.

21. Activate the NE Isometric view.

22.

Inspect the columns and beams.

23. Save as *ex6-3.dwg*.

Notes:

QUIZ 3

True or False

1. Custom content can be located in any subdirectory and still function properly.

2. The sole purpose of the Space Planning process is to arrange furniture in a floor plan.

3. The Design Center only has 3D objects stored in the Content area because ADT is strictly a 3D software.

4. Appliances are automatically placed on the APPLIANCE layer.

5. When you place a wall cabinet, it is automatically placed at the specified height.

6. You can create tools on a tool palette by dragging and dropping the objects from the Design Center onto the palette.

Multiple Choice

7. A residential structure is divided into:

   A. Four basic areas
   B. Three basic areas
   C. Two basic areas
   D. One basic area

8. Kitchen cabinets are located in the _____ subfolder.

   A. Casework
   B. Cabinets
   C. Bookcases
   D. Furniture

9. Select the area type that is NOT part of a private residence:

   A. Bedrooms
   B. Common Areas
   C. Service Areas
   D. Public Areas

10. To set the layer properties of a tool on a tool palette:

    A. Use the Layer Manager
    B. Select the tool, right click and select Properties
    C. Launch the Properties dialog
    D. All of the above

11. Vehicles placed from the Design Center are automatically placed on this layer:

    A. A-Site-Vhcl
    B. A-Vhcl
    C. C-Site Vhcl
    D. None of the above

12. The **Roof** tool is located on this tool palette:

    A. DESIGN
    B. GENERAL DRAFTING
    C. MASSING
    D. TOOLS

ANSWERS:

1) T; 2) F; 3) F; 4) F; 5) T; 6) T; 7) B; 8) A; 9) D; 10) B; 11) C; 12) A

Lesson 7
Rendering & Materials

AutoCAD Architecture divides materials into TWO locations:
Materials in Active Drawing
- Materials in Active Drawing
- Autodesk Library

You can also create one or more custom libraries for materials you want to use in more than one project. You can only edit materials in the drawing or in the custom library – Autodesk Materials are read-only.

Materials have two asset definitions –Appearance and Information. Materials do not have to be fully defined to be used. Each asset contributes to the definition of a single material.

You can define Appearance independently without assigning/associating it to a material. You can assign the same assets to different materials. Assets can be deleted from a material in a drawing or in a user library, but you can not remove or delete assets from materials in locked material libraries, such as the Autodesk Materials library or any locked user library. You can delete assets from a user library – BUT be careful because that asset might be used somewhere!

You can only duplicate, replace or delete an asset if it is in the drawing or in a user library. The Autodesk Asset Library is "read-only" and can only be used to check-out or create materials.

The Material Browser is divided into three distinct panels.

The Document Materials panel lists all the materials available in the drawing.

The Material Libraries list any libraries available.

The Library Materials lists the materials in the material libraries.

The search field allows you to search materials using keywords, description or comments.

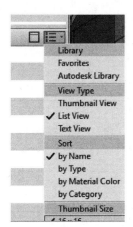

The View control button allows you to control how materials are sorted and displayed in the Material Libraries panel.

Material Editor

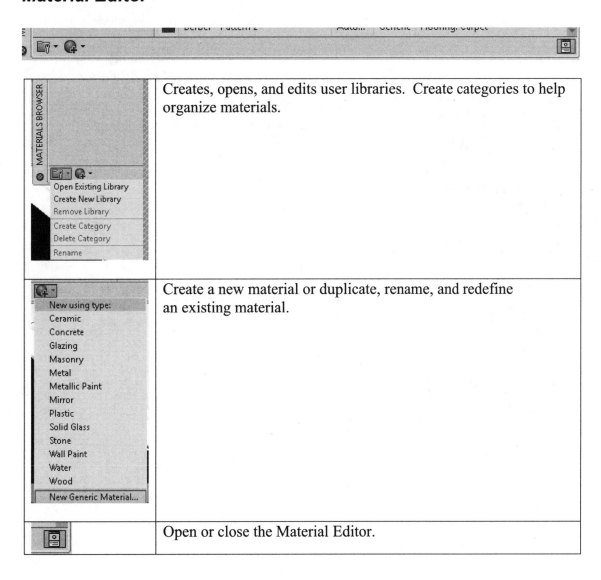

	Creates, opens, and edits user libraries. Create categories to help organize materials.
	Create a new material or duplicate, rename, and redefine an existing material.
	Open or close the Material Editor.

Exercise 7-1:
Modifying the Material Browser Interface

Drawing Name: ex6-3.dwg
Estimated Time: 10 minutes

This exercise reinforces the following skills:

❑   Navigating the Material Browser and Material Editor

1.

   Activate the **Render** ribbon.

   Select the small arrow in the lower right corner of the materials panel.

   This launches the Material Editor.

2.

   Launch the Material Browser by selecting the button on the bottom of the Material Editor dialog.

3.

Make the Material Browser appear as shown.

Toggle the Materials Library pane OFF by selecting the top button on the Libraries pane.

4.

Toggle the Materials Library list OFF by selecting the top button on the Documents pane.

5.

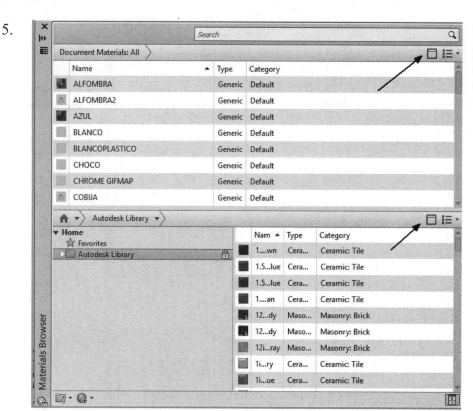

Toggle the panes ON by selecting the top button.

6. In the Document Materials panel, set the view to **Show Unused**.

Scroll through the list to see what materials are not being used in your drawing.

7. In the Material Library pane, change the view to sort **by Category**.

8. Close the Material dialogs.

9. Save as *ex7-1.dwg*.

The Appearance Tab

Appearance controls how material is displayed in a rendered view, Realistic view, or Ray Trace view.

A zero next to the hand means that only the active/selected material uses the appearance definition.

Different material types can have different appearance parameters.

The Information Tab

The value in the Description field can be used in Material tags.

Using comments and keywords can be helpful for searches.

Use this flow chart as a guide to help you decide whether or not you need to create a new material in your project.

Exercise 7-2:
Copy a Material from a Library to a Drawing

Drawing Name: ex7.1.rvt
Estimated Time: 10 minutes

In order to use or assign a material, it must exist in the drawing. You can search for a material and, if one exists in the Autodesk Library, copy it to your active drawing.

This exercise reinforces the following skills:

- Copying materials from the Autodesk Materials Library
- Modifying materials in the drawing

1. Go to the **Render** ribbon.

2. Select the **Materials Browser** tool.

3. Type **yellow** in the search field.

4. There are no yellow materials in the drawing.

Highlight **Wall Paint** under Autodesk Library.

There are three yellow wall paints.

5. Locate the Yellow Matte Wall Paint.

Select the up arrow to copy the material up to the drawing.

The yellow paint material is now listed in the Document Materials.

6. Type **blue** in the search field.

7.

There are no blue materials in the drawing, but the Autodesk Library has several different blue wall paints available.

8. Locate the **Periwinkle** Wall Paint and then copy it over to the drawing.

9. The blue wall paint is now available in the drawing.

10. Close the Materials dialog.

11. Save as *ex7-2.rvt*.

You have added material definitions to the active drawing ONLY.

Exercise 7-3:

Adding Color to Walls

Drawing Name: ex7-2.dwg
Estimated Time: 5 minutes

This exercise reinforces the following skills:

- ❑ Edit External Reference
- ❑ Materials
- ❑ Colors
- ❑ Display Manager
- ❑ Style Manager

1. Open *ex7-2.dwg*.

2. Zoom into the kitchen area. We are going to apply a different color to the kitchen wall.

    Select the wall indicated.

3. Right click and select **Edit Wall Style**.

    Notice that there are two GWB components.
    One GWB is for one side of the wall and one is for the other.

4. Rename them **GWB-Yellow** and **GWB-Blue**.

Index	Name	Priority	W
1	GWB-Yellow	1200	5/
2	Stud	500	4"
3	GWB-Blue	1200	5/

    To rename, just left click in the column and edit the text.

5. Activate the Materials tab.

    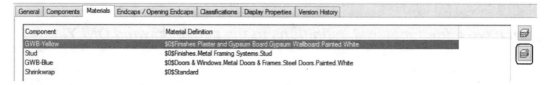

Component	Material Definition
GWB-Yellow	0Finishes.Plaster and Gypsum Board.Gypsum Wallboard Painted White
Stud	0Finishes.Metal Framing Systems.Stud
GWB-Blue	0Doors & Windows.Metal Doors & Frames.Steel Doors.Painted.White
Shrinkwrap	0Standard

    Highlight the **GWB-Yellow** component.
    Select the **New** button.

6. Type **Finishes.Wall Paint.Yellow.**

    Press **OK**.

7.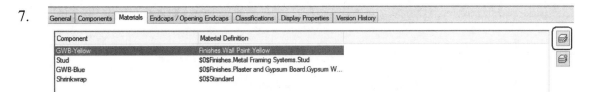

Highlight the **GWB-Yellow** component.
Select the **Edit** button.

8.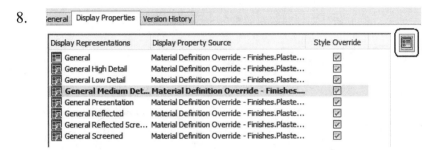

Activate the **Display Properties** tab.
Select the **Edit Display Properties** button.

9.

Activate the **Layer/Color/ Linetype** tab.

Highlight **3D Body**.

Left pick on the color square.

10.

Select the color **yellow**.

Press **OK**.

11.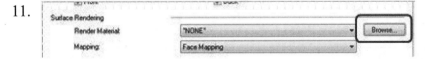

Select the **Other** tab.

Select **Browse** next to Render Material.

12.

Scroll down to the Yellow color.

Highlight and press **OK**.

Note that the materials are in alphabetic order.

13. Press **OK** to close the dialog.

14.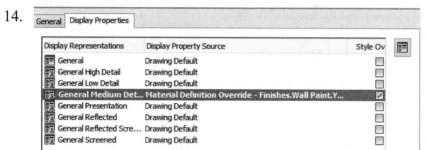

Verify that there is a check in the Style Override box.

Press **OK** again.

15.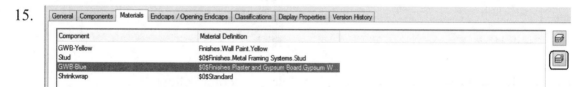

Highlight the **GWB-Blue** component.
Select the **New** button.

16. Type **Finishes.Wall Paint.Periwinkle**.

Press **OK**.

17.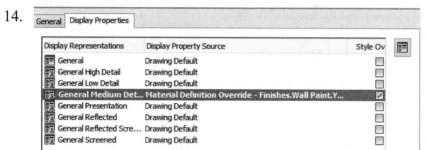

Highlight the **GWB-Blue** component.
Select the **Edit** button.

18. Activate the **Display Properties** tab. Select the **Edit Display Properties** button.

19. Activate the **Layer/Color/ Linetype** tab.

Highlight **3D Body**.

Left pick on the color square.

20. Select the color **blue**.

Press **OK**.

21. Select the **Other** tab.

Use the drop down list to select the color Periwinkle.

22. Verify that there is a check next to the Style Override.

Press **OK**.

23. Your components should show two different material definitions for the GWB components.

Press **OK**.

24. On the View ribbon:
Change the display to **Shaded**.

25. Inspect the walls.

Notice that all walls using the wall style have blue on one side and yellow on the other.

In order to apply different colors to different walls, you would have to create a wall style for each color assignment.

26. To flip the color so walls are yellow/blue, simply use the direction arrows.

27. Save as *ex7-3.dwg*.

Exercise 7-4:
Reference Manager

Drawing Name: ex4-4.dwg
Estimated Time: 5 minutes

This exercise reinforces the following skills:

    ❑   Reference Manager

1.   Open *ex4-4.dwg*.

2.   Activate the **Insert** ribbon.

Launch the Reference Manager by selecting the small arrow in the right corner of the Reference panel.

3.   Highlight the *ex3-8.dwg* file.

In the bottom pane, locate the Saved Path field.

4.

Change the Saved Path to *ex7-3.dwg*.
This updates the external reference and replaces ex3-8 with ex7-3.

5.   Select the Refresh button.

The file updates. Notice the structural members that were added in the previous lesson. The colors on the interior walls should also display properly in Shaded display mode.

6.   Save the file as *ex7-4.dwg*.

Exercise 7-5:

Camera View

Drawing Name: ex7-4.dwg
Estimated Time: 5 minutes

This exercise reinforces the following skills:

- ❑ Camera
- ❑ Display Settings

1. Open *ex7-4.dwg.*

2. Use the View Cube to orient the floor plan to a Top View with North in correct position.

3. Activate the Render ribbon.

    On the Camera panel:

    Select **Create Camera**.

4. Place the Camera so it is in the dining area and looking toward the kitchen.

    Press ENTER.
    Select the camera so it highlights.

5. A Camera Preview window will open.

    If you don't see the Camera Preview window, left click on the camera and the window should open.

    Set the Visual Style to **Shaded**.

6. Right click on the camera and select **Properties**.

Change the Camera Z value to **3′ 6″**.

This sets the camera at 3′ 6″ above floor level.

7. Note that the Preview Window updates.

8. Activate the View ribbon.

Notice the Camera1 view has been added to the view lists.

Left click to activate the Camera1 view.

9. Change the Display Style to **Conceptual**.

10. Set Materials/Textures **On**.

11. Set **Full Shadows** on.

12. Set **Realistic Face Style** on.

The Camera view should adjust as the different settings are applied.

13. Save as *ex7-5.dwg*.

Exercise 7-6:
Create Rendering

Drawing Name: ex7-5.dwg
Estimated Time: 5 minutes

This exercise reinforces the following skills:

- ❑ Render
- ❑ Display Settings

1.   Open *ex7-5.dwg*.

2.   Verify that the Camera1 view is active.

3.   Activate the Render ribbon.

            Verify that the Sun is turned on.

            Set the time to mid-afternoon.

4.   Full Shadows should be set to **ON**.

5.   Materials and Textures should be set to **ON**.

6.   On the Render to Size dropdown, select the **More Output Settings.**

7.   Set the Image Size to 1280x720 px.
    Set the Resolution to 600.
    Press Save.

8.

    Render to Size

    Click on **Render to Size**.

9. A window will come up where the camera view will be rendered.

    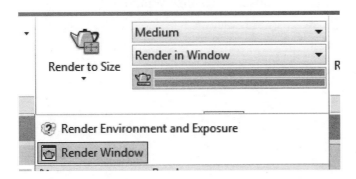

    If you don't see the window, use the drop-down to open the Render Window.

10. Select the save icon to save the rendered image.

11. Save the image file to the exercise folder.

| File name: | kitchen-render1 |
| Files of type: | JPEG(*.jpeg,*.jpg) |

12. Accept the defaults and press **OK**.

Close the Render Window.

JPG Image Options

Quality:

96

Draft — Best

File Size: 144 KB

OK   Cancel

13. Save as *ex7-6.dwg*.

Exercise 7-7:
Render in Cloud

Drawing Name: ex7-6.dwg
Estimated Time: 5 minutes

This exercise reinforces the following skills:

  ❏   Render in Cloud
  ❏   Autodesk 360

Autodesk offers a service where you can render your model on their server using an internet connection. You need to register for an account. Educators and students can create a free account. The advantage of using the Cloud for rendering is that you can continue to work while the rendering is being processed.

1.   Open *ex7-6.dwg*.

2.   Verify that the Camera1 view is active.

3.   In order to render using Autodesk's Cloud Service, you need to sign in to an Autodesk 360 account. Registration is free and storage is free to students and educators.

      Sign in to your Autodesk 360 account.

4.   Activate the Render ribbon.

      Select **Render in Cloud**.

5.   Set the Model View to render the current view.

      Click the **Start Rendering** model.

6.

Creating Online Render Job...

You should see a small window showing that the rendering operation is in process.

7.

A small bubble message will appear when the rendering is completed.

8.

You will receive an email when the rendering is complete.

9.

Select **Render Gallery** on the Render ribbon to see your renderings.

Compare the quality of the rendering performed using the Cloud with the rendering done in the previous exercise.

I have found that rendering using Autodesk 360 is faster and produces better quality images.

Lesson 8
Documentation

Before we can create our construction drawings, we need to create layouts or views to present the design. AutoCAD Architecture is similar to AutoCAD in that the user can work in Model and Paper Space. Model Space is where we create the 3D model of our house. Paper Space is where we create or set up various views that can be used in our construction drawings. In each view, we can control what we see by turning off layers, zooming, panning, etc.

To understand paper space and model space, imagine a cardboard box. Inside the cardboard box is Model Space. This is where your 3D model is located. On each side of the cardboard box, tear out a small rectangular window. The windows are your viewports. You can look through the viewports to see your model. To reach inside the window so you can move your model around or modify it, you double-click inside the viewport. If your hand is not reaching through any of the windows and you are just looking from the outside, then you are in Paper Space or Layout mode.

You can create an elevation in your current drawing by first drawing an elevation line and mark, and then creating a 2D or 3D elevation based on that line. You can control the size and shape of the elevation that is generated. Unless you explode the elevation that you create, the elevation remains linked to the building model that you used to create it. Because of this link between the elevation and the building model, any changes to the building model can be made in the elevation as well.

When you create a 2D elevation, the elevation is created with hidden and overlapping lines removed. You can edit the 2D elevation that you created by changing its display properties. The 2D Section/Elevation style allows you to add your own display components to the display representation of the elevation, and create rules that assign different parts of the elevation to different display components. You can control the visibility, layer, color, linetype, lineweight, and linetype scale of each component. You can also use the line work editing commands to assign individual lines in your 2D elevation to display components, and merge geometry into your 2D elevation.

After you create a 2D elevation, you can use the AutoCAD BHATCH and AutoCAD DIMLINEAR commands to hatch and dimension the 2D elevation.

AutoCAD Architecture comes with standard title block templates. They are located in the Templates subdirectory under *Program Data \ Autodesk\ ACA 2016 \enu \Template*.

If you are using VISTA or Windows 7, the templates are stored under *Users/<user name>/AppData/Local/ Autodesk/AutoCAD 2016/R18.2/enu/Template*.

Many companies will place their templates on the network so all users can access the same templates. In order to make this work properly, set the Options so that the templates folder is pointed to the correct path.

Exercise 8-1:

Creating a Custom Titleblock

Drawing Name: Architectural Title Block.dwg
Estimated Time: 30 minutes

This exercise reinforces the following skills:

- ❑ Title blocks
- ❑ Attributes
- ❑ Edit Block In-Place
- ❑ Insert Image
- ❑ Insert Hyperlink

1.   Select the **Open** tool.

2.   Set the Files of type to *Drawing Template*.

3. Browse to
   *ProgramData\Autodesk\ACA 2016\enu\ Template\AutoCAD
   Templates*.

4.   Open the *Tutorial-iArch.dwt*.
   Verify that *Files of type* is set to Drawing Template or
   you won't see the file.

5.   Perform a **File→Save as**.

   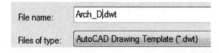 Save the file to your work folder.
   Rename **Arch_D.dwt**.

6.   Enter a description and press **OK**.

7. Firm Name and Address Zoom into the Firm Name and Address rectangle.

8. **A** Select the **MTEXT** tool from the **Annotation** panel on the Home ribbon.

   Multiline Text Draw a rectangle to place the text.

9. Set the Font to **Verdana**.

   Hint: If you type the first letter of the font, the drop-down list will jump to fonts starting with that letter.

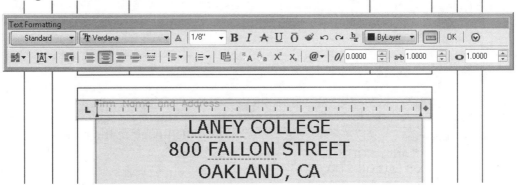

LANEY COLLEGE
800 FALLON STREET
OAKLAND, CA

   Set the text height to ⅛″.
   Set the justification to **centered**.
   Enter the name and address of your college.

10.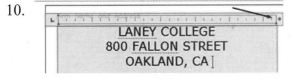

LANEY COLLEGE
800 FALLON STREET
OAKLAND, CA

   Extend the ruler to change the width of your MTEXT box to fill the rectangle.

   Press **OK**.

11.

Firm Name and Address

**LANEY COLLEGE
800 FALLON STREET
OAKLAND, CA**

Use **MOVE** to locate the text properly, if needed.

12. Activate the **Insert** ribbon.

Select the arrow located on the right bottom of the Reference panel.

13. The External Reference Manager will launch.

Select **Attach Image** from the drop-down list.

14. Locate the image file you wish to use.
There is an image file available for use from the publisher's website called *college logo.jpg*.
Press **Open**.

15. Press **OK**.

16.

Firm Name and Address

**LANEY COLLEGE
800 FALLON STREET
OAKLAND, CA**

Place the image in the rectangle.

If you are concerned about losing the link to the image file (for example, if you plan to email this file to another person), you can use **INSERTOBJ** to embed the image into the drawing. Do not enable link to create an embedded object. The INSERTOBJ command is not available on the standard ribbon.

17. Select the image.
    Right click and select **Properties**.

18.
    Select the **Extended** tab.
    Pick the Hyperlink field.

19.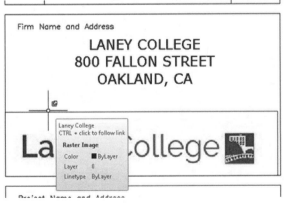

    Type in the name of the school in the Text to display field.

    Type in the website address in the *Type the file or Web page name* field.

    Press **OK**.
    Close the Properties dialog.

20.
    If you hover your mouse over the image, you will see a small icon. This indicates there is a hyperlink attached to the image. To launch the webpage, simply hold down the CTRL key and left click on the icon.

If you are unsure of the web address of the website you wish to link, use the Browse for **Web Page** button.

21.

Firm Name and Address

LANEY COLLEGE
800 FALLON STREET
OAKLAND, CA

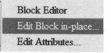

To turn off the image frame/boundary:

Type **IMAGEFRAME** at the command line. Enter **0**.

IMAGEFRAME has the following options:

        0: Turns off the image frame and does not plot
        1: Turns on the image frame and is plotted
        2: Turns on the image frame, but does not plot

22.

Block Editor
Edit Block in-place...
Edit Attributes...

Select the titleblock.
Right click and select **Edit Block in-place**.

23. Press **OK**.

24. Change the text for Project to **Drafter**.
To change, simply double click on the text and an edit box will appear.

Text	
Layer	0
Contents	Drafter
Style	Roman
Annotative	No
Justify	Left
Height	1/16"
Rotation	0d0'0"

Project

25. Select the **Define Attribute** tool from the Insert ribbon.

Define
Attributes

26. Select the **Field** tool.

27. Highlight Author and Uppercase.

Field category:
All

Field names:
Author
BlockPlaceholder
Comments
CreateDate
CurrentSheetCategory
CurrentSheetCustom

Author:

Format:
(none)
Uppercase
Lowercase
First capital
Title case

Press **OK**.

28.

Mode	Attribute
Invisible	Tag: DRAFTER
Constant	Prompt: DRAFTER
Verify	Default: ----
Preset	
✓ Lock position	**Text Settings**
Multiple lines	Justification: Left
Insertion Point	Text style: Standard
Specify on-screen	Annotative
X: 2' 6.5"	Text height: 1/8"
Y: 2 1/16'	Rotation: 0d0'0"
Z: 0"	Boundary width: 0"
Align below previous attribute definition	

In the Tag field, enter **DRAFTER**.
In the Prompt field, enter
DRAFTER.
The Value field is used by the
FIELD property.
In the Insertion Point area:
In the X field, enter: **2' 6.5"**.
In the Y field, enter: **2-1/16"**.
In the Z field, enter: **0"**.
In the Text Options area:
Set the Justification to **Left**.
Set the Text Style to **Standard**.
Set the Height to **1/8"**.

Press **OK**.

29. Select the **Define Attributes** tool.

Define
Attributes

30.

Mode	Attribute
Invisible	Tag: DATE
Constant	Prompt: DATE
Verify	Default: 8/5/2012
Preset	
✓ Lock position	**Text Settings**
Multiple lines	Justification: Left
Insertion Point	Text style: Standard
Specify on-screen	Annotative
X: 2' 6.5"	Text height: 1/8"
Y: 1 9/16'	Rotation: 0d0'0"
Z: 0"	Boundary width: 0"
Align below previous attribute definition	

In the Tag field, enter **DATE**.
In the Prompt field, enter **DATE**.

In the Insertion Point area:
In the X field, enter: **2' 6.5"**.
In the Y field, enter: **1-9/16"**.
In the Z field, enter: **0"**.
In the Text Options area:
Set the Justification to **Left**.
Set the Text Style to **Standard**.
Set the Height to **1/8"**.

31. Select the Field button to set the default value for the attribute.

CurrentSheetTitle	1:30:59 PM
DatabaseField	13:30
Date	13:30:59
DeviceName	Sunday, August 05, 2012 (Regior
DieselExpression	Sunday, August 05, 2012 1:30:5
Filename	8/5/2012 (Regional short date)
Filesize	8/5/2012 1:30:59 PM (Regional s
Formula	1:30:59 PM (Regional time)

Select **Date**.
Set the Date format to **Regional short date**.

Press **OK**.

32. Select the **Define Attributes** tool.

Define
Attributes

33.

In the Tag field, enter **SCALE**.
In the Prompt field, enter **SCALE**.
In the Insertion Point area:
In the X field, enter: **2′ 6.5″**.
In the Y field, enter: **1-1/16″**.
In the Z field, enter: **0″**.
In the Text Options area:
Set the Justification to **Left**.
Set the Text Style to **Standard**.
Set the Height to **1/8″**.

34.

Select the Field button to set the default value for the attribute.

Select **PlotScale**.
Set the format to **1:#**.

Press **OK**.

Press **OK** to place the attribute.

35. Select the **Define Attributes** tool.

Define
Attributes

36.

In the Tag field, enter **SHEETNO**.
In the Prompt field, enter **SHEET NO**.
In the Insertion Point area:
In the X field, enter: **2′ 8.25″**
In the Y field, enter: **1-9/16″**
In the Z field, enter: **0**
In the Text Options area:
Set the Justification to **Left**.
Set the Text Style to **Standard**.
Set the Height to **1/8″**.

37.

Select the Field button to set the default value for the attribute.

Select **CurrentSheetNumber**.
Set the format to **Uppercase**.

Press **OK**.

Press **OK** to place the attribute.

38. Select the **Define Attribute** tool.

Define
Attributes

39.

In the Tag field, enter
PROJECTNAME.
In the Prompt field, enter **PROJECT NAME**.
  In the Insertion Point area:
    In the X field, enter: **2′ 7-9/16″**
    In the Y field, enter: **4″**
    In the Z field, enter: **0**
  In the Text Options area:
    Set the Justification to **Center**.
    Set the Text Style to **Standard**.
    Set the Height to **1/8″**.

40. Select the Field button to set the default value for the attribute.

Select **AEC Project** for the field category.
Set the Field Name to **Project Name**.
Set the format to **Uppercase**.

Press **OK**.

A common error for students is to forget to enter the insertion point. The default insertion point is set to 0,0,0. If you don't see your attributes, look for them at the lower left corner of your title block and use the MOVE tool to position them appropriately.

Your title block should look similar to the image shown.

If you like, you can use the MOVE tool to reposition any of the attributes to make them fit better.

41. Select **Save** on the ribbon to save the changes to the title block and exit the Edit Block In-Place mode.

42. Press **OK**.

43. Save the file and go to **File→Close**.

> Use templates to standardize how you want your drawing sheets to look. Store your templates on a server so everyone in your department uses the same titleblock and sheet settings. You can also set up dimension styles and layer standards in your templates.

> ADT 2005 introduced a new tool available when you are in Paper Space that allows you to quickly switch to the model space of a viewport without messing up your scale. Simply select the **Maximize Viewport** button located on your task bar to switch to model space.

> To switch back to paper space, select the **Minimize Viewport** button.

You use the Project Navigator to create additional drawing files with the desired views for your model. The views are created on the Views tab of the Project Navigator. You then create a sheet set which gathers together all the necessary drawing files that are pertinent to your project.

Previously, you would use external references, which would be external drawing files that would be linked to a master drawing. You would then create several layout sheets in your master drawing that would show the various views. Some users placed all their data in a single drawing and then used layers to organize the data.

This shift in the way of organizing your drawings will mean that you need to have a better understanding of how to manage all the drawings. It also means you can leverage the drawings so you can reuse the same drawing in more than one sheet set.

You can create five different types of views using the Project Navigator:

- ❑ Model Space View – a portion that is displayed in its own viewport. This view can have a distinct name, display configuration, description, layer snapshot and drawing scale.
- ❑ Detail View – displays a small section of the model, i.e., a wall section, plumbing, or foundation. This type of view is usually associated with a callout. It can be placed in your current active drawing or in a new drawing.
- ❑ Section View – displays a building section, usually an interior view. This type of view is usually associated with a callout. It can be placed in your current active drawing or in a new drawing.
- ❑ Elevation View – displays a building elevation, usually an exterior view. This type of view is usually associated with a callout. It can be placed in your current active drawing or in a new drawing.
- ❑ Sheet View – this type of view is created when a model space view is dropped onto a layout sheet.

Note: Some classes have difficulty using the Project Navigator because they do not use the same work station each class, or the drawings are stored on a network server. In those cases, the links can be lost and the students get frustrated trying to get the correct results.

Exercise 8-2:

Verifying the Project Setting

Drawing Name: ex7-7.dwg
Estimated Time: 5 minutes

This exercise reinforces the following skills:

- ❑ Project Navigator
- ❑ Project Browser

1. Open *ex7-7.dwg*.

2.   Right click in the command window and select **Options**.

3. Select the **AEC Project Defaults** tab.

4. 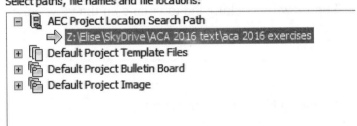 Verify that the AEC Project Location Search Path connects to the location where you are saving your files.

5. Press **OK** to close the Options dialog.

6. Launch the **Project Navigator** from the Quick Access toolbar.

7. Verify that the Current Project is set to the Brown Residence project.

8. To set the active project, select the tool on the lower part of the palette.

9.   Right click on the **Brown Residence** project and select **Set Project Current**.

10. Save as *ex8-2.dwg*.

Tags and schedules use project information. If you do not have a current project defined, you may see some error messages when you tag elements.

Exercise 8-3:
Creating Elevation Views

Drawing Name: ex8-2.dwg
Estimated Time: 15 minutes

This exercise reinforces the following skills:

- ❏ Creating an Elevation View
- ❏ Adding a Callout
- ❏ Named Views

1.   Open *ex8-2.dwg*.

2.   Switch to the Model tab.

3.   Activate the **Top** view by clicking the top plane on the view cube.

4.   Spin the View cube so North is oriented on top.

5.   Set the view to **2D Wireframe** mode by selecting the View Display in the upper left corner of the window.

6.   Use **Zoom Extents** to view the entire model.

7.   Thaw the **A-Roof-Slab** and **A-Roof** layers.

8. Launch the **Design Tools** palette.

9. Right click on the grey bar on the left of the Design palette.

Enable the **Document** palette.

10. Activate the **Annotation** tab.

11. 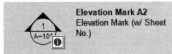 Scroll down and locate **Elevation Mark A2**.

12. Place the elevation mark below the model.
Use your cursor to orient the arrow toward the building model.

13. Set your view name to: **South Elevation**.

Enable **Generate Section/Elevation**.

Enable **Place Titlemark**.

Set the Scale to **1/8″ = 1′-0″**.

Press the **Current Drawing** button.

14. Window around the entire building to select it.
Select the upper left corner above the building and the lower right corner below the building.

15. Place the elevation to the right of the view.

Zoom into the elevation view, so you can inspect it.

16. To activate the elevation view, select it from the View list located on the View ribbon.

17. Save as *ex8-3.dwg*.

Exercise 8-4
Editing an Elevation View

Drawing Name: ex8-3.dwg
Estimated Time: 15 minutes

This exercise reinforces the following skills:

- ❑ Modifying an External Reference
- ❑ Materials Browser
- ❑ Editing a Style

1. Open *ex8-3.dwg*.

2. Activate the **Top** view from the View ribbon or using the View cube.

3. Select the model.
    Then select Open Reference on the ribbon.

4. Verify that the A-Roof-Slab layer is thawed and on.

5. Freeze the image layer.

6. Activate the Render ribbon.

Launch the Materials Browser.

7. Highlight Roofing in the left pane to see the shake roofing materials listed.

Highlight **Shake-Handsplit** and copy to the active document.

8. Once the material is copied, you should see it listed in the active document.

Close the Materials Browser.

9. Select a roof slab.

10. Right click and select **Edit Roof Slab Style.**

11.

Component	Material Definition	
Asphalt Shingles	Asphalt Shingles	
Membrane	Membrane	
Plywood Sheathing	Plywood Sheathing	
Shrink Wrap Body	Standard	

Select the Materials tab.
Highlight the Asphalt Shingles component.
Select the Edit Material Definition on the right.

12.

Layer/Color/Linetype | Hatching | Other

Surface Hatch Placement
☑ Top   ☑ Bottom
☑ Left   ☑ Right
☑ Front   ☑ Back

Surface Rendering
Render Material: Shake - Handsplit   ∨   Browse...
Mapping: Face Mapping   ∨

Live Section Rendering
Cut Surface Render Material: Thermal & Moisture.Shingles.Asphalt Shingles.Deep Shadc ∨   Browse...
Sectioned Body Render Material: Thermal & Moisture.Shingles.Asphalt Shingles.Deep Shadc ∨   Browse...

2D Section/Elevation Rules

Select the Other tab.
Set the Render Material to the **Shake- Handsplit.**

Press **OK.**

13.

General | Display Properties

Display Representations	Display Property Source	Style Override
General	Drawing Default	☐
General High Detail	Drawing Default	☐
General Low Detail	Drawing Default	☐
General Medium Det...	Material Definition Override - Wood S...	☑
General Presentation	Drawing Default	☐
General Reflected	Drawing Default	☐
General Reflected Scre...	Drawing Default	☐
General Screened	Drawing Default	☐

Verify that the Style Override is enabled.

14. Press **OK.**
Press ESC to release the roof slab that is selected.

15. Save the file and close.

16.

File References

Reference ...	Status	Size
ex8-3*	Opened	6.64 MB
Building Model ⚠	Needs reloading	1.44 MB
Building Mod...	Loaded	93.6 KB
sofa andy3	Loaded	294 KB

Open the Reference Manager.

The Reference Manager notes that the Building Model needs to be reloaded.

Right click and select **Reload.**

17.

Select the elevation line in the top view.

18. Select **Generate Elevation** from the ribbon.

Generate Elevation

19.

Right click to select **Dialog.**

20.

Enable **Replace Existing**.

Select the **Select Object** button.

Select the 2D Elevation placed in the previous exercise.

Press **OK**.

21. The elevation view updates.

If you still do not see the shake hatch pattern, check the scale of the hatch pattern to ensure it is set low enough to be visible in the elevation view.

22. Save as *ex8-4.dwg*.

Exercise 8-5:
Creating Layouts

Drawing Name: ex8-4.dwg
Estimated Time: 25 minutes

This exercise reinforces the following skills:

- ❑ Create Layout
- ❑ Adding a View to a Layout
- ❑ Control Visibility of elements using Layers

1.   Open *ex8-4.dwg*.

2.   Right click on the command line and select **Options**.

                       You can also type OPTIONS.

3.   Activate the **Display** tab.

                       Enable **Display Layout and Model tabs**.

                       Press **OK**.

4.   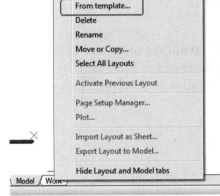   Right click on the Work tab.

                       Select **From template**.

5.   Browse to your exercise folder.

     Select the *Arch_D* template.
     Press **Open**.

6.   Press **OK**.

7.   Activate the **D-Size Layout**.

8.

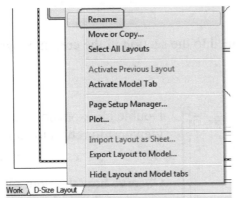

Right click on the **D-Size Layout** tab.

Select **Rename**.

9. Rename Floorplan.

10.

Select the viewport.

Set Display locked to **No**.

11.

Resize the viewport to only show the floor plan.

Double click inside the viewport to activate model space.

Pan the model to position inside the viewport.

12. Activate the Home ribbon.

Freeze the layer assigned to roof slabs in the current viewport.

13.

The view updates with no roof.

Select the section line used to define the south elevation.

14. Activate the Home ribbon.

Freeze the layer assigned to the section in the current viewport.

15.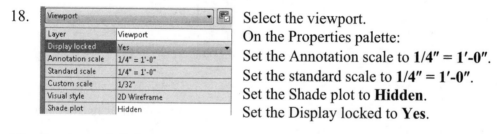

Double click outside the viewport to return to paper space.

Observe how the floor plan view has changed.

16. Activate the Home ribbon.

Launch the Layer Manager.

17. Scroll down to the Viewport layer.
Set the Viewport layer to DO NOT PLOT.

The viewports can be visible so you can adjust them but will not appear in prints.

Close the Layer Manager dialog.

18. Select the viewport.
On the Properties palette:
Set the Annotation scale to **1/4″ = 1′-0″**.
Set the standard scale to **1/4″ = 1′-0″**.
Set the Shade plot to **Hidden**.
Set the Display locked to **Yes**.

19. Save as *ex8-5.dwg*.

Exercise 8-6:
Creating a Sheet

Drawing Name: ex8-5.dwg
Estimated Time: 15 minutes

This exercise reinforces the following skills:

- ❑ Layouts
- ❑ Viewports

1. Open *ex8-5.dwg*.

2. If your layout tabs are not displayed:
    Right click on the command line and select **Options**.

    You can also type OPTIONS.

3.   Activate the **Display** tab.

    Enable **Display Layout and Model tabs**.

    Press **OK**.

4. Right click on the + tab.

    Select **From template**.

5. 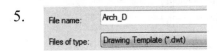 Browse to the folder where you are saving your work.
    Select the *Arch_D* template.
    Press **Open**.

6. Press **OK**.

7.   Activate the **D-Size Layout**.

8.

Right click on the **D-Size Layout** tab.

Select **Rename**.

9. Rename **South Elevation**.

10. Select the viewport.
Right click and set the Display locked to **No**.

11. Double click inside the viewport to activate model space.

12.

Left click inside the viewport and then position the elevation view inside the viewport.

13.

Layer	Viewport
Display locked	Yes
Annotation scale	1/4" = 1'-0"
Standard scale	1/4" = 1'-0"
Custom scale	1/32"
Visual style	2D Wireframe
Shade plot	Hidden

Select the viewport.
Set the Annotation scale to **1/4″ = 1′-0″ [1:100]**.
Set the Standard scale to **1/4″= 1′-0″ [1:100]**.

Set the Shade plot to **Hidden**.

You may need to re-center the view in the viewport after you change the scale. Use PAN to do this so the scale does not change.

Lock the display.

14. Save the file as *ex8-6.dwg*.

Tips
Tricks

➢ By locking the Display you ensure your model view will not accidentally shift if you activate the viewport.

➢ The Annotation Plot Size value can be restricted by the Linear Precision setting on the Units tab. If the Annotation Plot Size value is more precise than the Linear Precision value, then the Annotation Plot Size value is not accepted.

Exercise 8-7

Modify a Dimension Style

Drawing Name: ex8-6.dwg
Estimated Time: 15 minutes

This exercise reinforces the following skills:

- ❑ Dimension Styles
- ❑ AEC Dimensions

1. Open *ex8-6.dwg*.

2. Activate the Annotate ribbon.

    Select the **Dimension Style Editor** on the Dimensions panel.

3. Highlight **Annotative**.

4. Select **Modify**.

5. On the Lines tab:

    Set the Baseline spacing to **1/2"**.

6. Set Extend beyond dim lines to **1/8"**.
    Set Offset from origin to **1/4"**.

7.
    On the Symbols and Arrows tab:

    Set the Arrow size to **1/4"**.

8.

On the Text tab:

Set the Text height to **1/4″**.

9.

Set the Offset from dim line to **1/8″**.

10.

Set the Text alignment to **Horizontal.**

11. Activate the Primary Units tab.

Set the Unit format to **Architectural.**
Set the Precision to **1/4″**.

12. Press **OK** and **Close**.

13. Save as *ex8-7.dwg*.

Exercise 8-8

Dimensioning a Floor Plan

Drawing Name: ex8-7.dwg
Estimated Time: 30 minutes

This exercise reinforces the following skills:

- ❑ Drawing Setup
- ❑ AEC Dimensions
- ❑ Title Mark
- ❑ Attributes
- ❑ Layouts

1. Open *ex8-7.dwg*.

2. 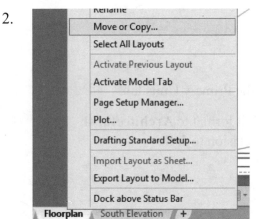 Highlight the **Floor Plan** layout tab.

   Right click and select **Move or Copy**.

3. Enable **Create a copy**.

   Highlight **(move to end)**.

   Press **OK**.

4. Model / Work / Floorplan / South Elevation / Floorplan (2) /   Select the second layout.

5. 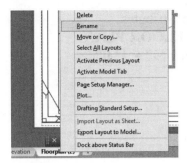 Highlight the second layout tab.

Right click and select **Rename**.

6. Modify the layout name to **A102 02 FLOOR PLAN**.

7. Launch the Annotation tools from the Annotate ribbon.

8. ![More Annotation Tools] Scroll down the tool palette.

Select **More Annotation Tools** to launch the Content Browser.

9. ![Search title] Search for **title**.

10. ![Title Mark] Locate the **Title Mark** indicated.

11. ![Title Mark / Elevation Mark A2] Drag and drop the Title Mark onto the Annotation tab of the Document palette.

12. Double click inside the viewport to activate model space.

13. ![Title] Select the **Title Mark** tool from the palette.
Pick below the view to place the title mark.

14. Pick two points to indicate the start and end points of the title mark.

Place the title mark below the view.

15.

Block Reference	
Layer	G-Anno-Ttlb
Name	Anno_Title_T2
Rotation	0.00
Annotative scale	1/4" = 1'-0"
TITLE	FLOOR PLAN
SCALE	1/4" = 1'-0"

Double click to edit the attributes.
In the Title field, enter **FLOOR PLAN**.
In the SCALE field, enter **¼″ = 1′-0″**.

Press **OK**.

16. FLOOR PLAN
1/4″ = 1′ − 0″

The view title updates.

17.

A

Multili
Text

Activate the Home ribbon.

In the Layers panel drop-down,

Select **Select Layer Standard**.

18.

Default Layer Standard
Layer Key Style:
AIA (256 Color) *current drawing
Description:

Set the Layer Key Style to **AIA (256 Color)**.

Press **OK**.

19.

Select the **AEC Dimension - Exterior** tool on the Annotate ribbon.

This tool is also available on the Dimensions tab of the Annotation tool palette.

Add Wall Dimensions is only available in Model Space. Dimensions are automatically placed on A-Anno-Dim layer when the Layering Standard is set to AIA.

20.

Select the walls, doors, and windows indicated on the right side of the building.

Press ENTER to complete the selection.

21.

Pick to the right of the building to place the dimensions.

All dimensions relevant to the wall will be placed.

22. Select the Dimension you just placed.
Select **Remove Extension Lines** from the ribbon.

Remove
Ext. Lines

23. Select the grips on the extension lines that are not necessary.
You should see a tool tip indicating the extension line to remove.

Remove extension Line

The selected lines will be deleted.

24. To add an extension line:
Select the AEC Dimension.

Select the Add Extension Lines tool from the ribbon.   Add Extension Lines
Then select the midpoint of the object to be dimensioned.
Then select the AEC Dimension.

25. 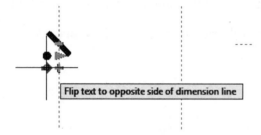 When you are done modifying the AEC Dimension, press ENTER to update the dimensions.

26. If the text landed on top of the building, look for a blue arrow. You can left click on it to flip the side the text is placed.

Flip text to opposite side of dimension line

27. Unsaved Layer State   A-Anno-Dims   Select the dimension.

The dimension should automatically be placed on A-Anno-Dims because the Layer Standard was set to AIA.

28. Switch back to Paper space.

PAPER

29. Save as *ex8-8.dwg*.

You can insert blocks into model or paper space. Note that you did not need to activate the viewport in order to place the Scale block.

Exercise 8-9

Create a Wall Section

Drawing Name: ex8-8.dwg
Estimated Time: 15 minutes

This exercise reinforces the following skills:

- ❏ Drawing Setup
- ❏ Dimension Styles
- ❏ AEC Dimensions
- ❏ Layouts

1. Open *ex8-8.dwg*.

2. Activate the Model layout tab.

3. Activate the **Annotate** ribbon.

   Select the **Section (Sheet Tail)** tool.

4. Draw the section through the south wall of the garage area.

   Select a point below the wall.
   Select a point above the wall.
   Right click and select ENTER.
   Left click to the right of the section line to indicate the section depth.

5.

Type Exterior Wall Section in the View Name field.

Enable Current Drawing.

Enable Generate Section/Elevation.

Enable Place Title mark.
Set the Scale to 1/8″ = 1′-0″.

6.

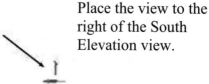

Place the view to the right of the South Elevation view.

7.

Select the view title for the wall section.

Type **1/8″ = 1′-0″** for the SCALE.

Type **Exterior Wall Section** for the TITLE.

Press ESC to release and update.

8.

Select the View title bubble.

Type **S1.1** for the NUMBER.

Press ESC to release and update.

9.

Highlight the **Floor Plan** layout tab.

Right click and select **Move or Copy**.

10. 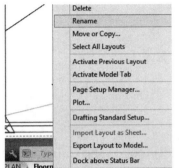 Enable **Create a copy**.

Highlight **(move to end)**.

Press **OK**.

11. `Model / Work / Floorplan / South Elevation \ Floorplan (2) /`   Select the second layout.

12.   Highlight the second layout tab.

Right click and select **Rename**.

13. `)R PLAN \ S1.2 Details /`   Modify the layout name to **S1.2 Details**.

14. Unlock the viewport.
     Position the Exterior Wall Section in the viewport.
     Adjust the size of the viewport.

Viewport	
Layer	Viewport
Display locked	Yes
Annotation scale	1/4" = 1'-0"
Standard scale	1/4" = 1'-0"
Custom scale	1/32"
Visual style	2D Wireframe
Shade plot	As Displayed

Select the viewport.
Set the Annotation scale to **1/4″ = 1′0″**.
Set the Standard scale to **1/4″ = 1′0″**.

Set the Shade plot to **As Displayed**.

Lock the display.

15. Press ESC to release the viewport.

16. Save as *ex8-9.dwg*.

Create a Section View

Drawing Name: ex8-9.dwg
Estimated Time: 10 minutes

This exercise reinforces the following skills:

    ❑   Sections

1.   Open *ex8-9.dwg.*

2.   [Work \ Floorplan \ Sout]   Activate the **Model** layout tab.
    Activate Model space.

3.   Activate the Annotate ribbon.

    Select the **Section (Sheet Tail)** tool on the Callouts panel.

4.   Draw a horizontal line through the master bathroom walls as shown.

5.   Name the View: **Master Bath Elevation**.
    Enable Generate Section/Elevation.
    Enable Place Titlemark.
    Set the Scale to **1/2″ = 1′-0″**.

    Place the view in the current drawing to the right of the building.

6. Switch to the Model tab and move the view to the right away from all the other views.

7. Highlight the **Floor Plan** layout tab.

    Right click and select **Move or Copy**.

8. Enable **Create a copy**.

    Highlight **(move to end)**.

    Press **OK**.

9. Select the second layout.

10. Highlight the second layout tab.

    Right click and select **Rename**.

11. Rename the layout name to **Master Bath Elevation**.

12.   Unlock the viewport display.

Position and resize the viewport to show the Master Bath Elevation.

13.   Change the values of the view title attributes as shown.

14. Save as *ex8-10.dwg*.

To create an elevation view with different visual styles, create a camera view.

Exercise 8-11

Add a Callout

Drawing Name: ex8-10.dwg
Estimated Time: 45 minutes

This exercise reinforces the following skills:

- ❑ Callouts
- ❑ Detail Component Manager
- ❑ Detail Elements
- ❑ Layouts
- ❑ Keynotes

1. Open *ex8-10.dwg*.

2.   Activate the **Model** layout tab.

3.

Zoom into the Exterior Wall Section view.

4.

Launch the Annotation Tools from the Annotate ribbon.

5.

Select the **Detail Boundary B** callout tool on the Callouts tab.

If you do not see this tool, verify that your profile is set to AutoCAD Architecture (US Imperial).

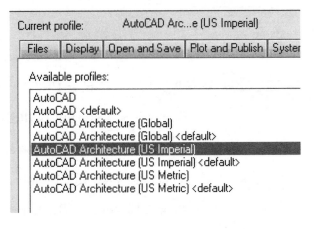

6.

Draw a small rectangle to designate the callout location.

7.

Select the starting and end point for the leader line.
Left click to the side of the wall section to place the label.

Press **ENTER** or right click to accept.

8.

Type **Detail of Exterior Wall Section** in the View Name field.

Enable **Generate Section/Elevation**.

Enable **Place Titlemark**.

Set the Scale to **1'-0" = 1'-0"**.

9.

Click on the **Current Drawing** button and place the view to the right of the section view.

10.

Select the view title for the wall section.

Type **1'-0" = 1'-0"** for the SCALE.

Type **Exterior Wall Detail** for the TITLE.

Press ESC to release and update.

11.

Layer	0
Name	Anno_Title_A1
Rotation	0.00
Annotative scale	1/2" = 1'-0"
NUMBER	D12

Select the View title bubble.

Type **D12** for the NUMBER.

Press ESC to release and update.

12.

13.

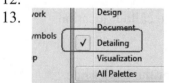

Right click on the Tool palette's bar.

Enable the Detailing palette.

14.   04 - Masonry   Select the **04- Masonry** detail tool on the Basic tab.

15.

Select the endpoint indicated to place the detail.

Select the top of the wall as the endpoint.

16.

Locate the 5/8" Gypsum Wallboard tool on the Interiors tab.

17.

Select the two inside corners to place this detail.

18. 3-1/2" Acoustical Batt Ins...

Select the 3-1/2" Acoustical Batt Insulation tool on the Interiors tab.

19.

Select the midpoints at the top and bottom of the section.

20. Select the 2x4 Detail on the Interiors palette.

21. Place four studs in the stud section.

22. Activate the DOCUMENT tool palette.

23.

Select the Annotation tab.

Select the **Reference Keynote (Straight Leader)**.

24. Select a top brick detail component.
Select the start and end point of the leader line.
Set the text width to **4'0"**.
Press ENTER.

25. Select the text.
Right click and select Properties.
In the Height field, set the text height to **1/32"**.

26. The keynote text updates.

27. Select the **Reference Keynote (Straight Leader).**
Select the 2x4 detail component.
Select the start and end point for the leader.
Set the text width to **4'0"**.
Press ENTER.
Select the text.
Right click and select Properties.
In the Height field, set the text height to **1/32"**.
Set the arrowhead size to 1/32".

Arrowhead	Closed filled
Arrowhead Size	1/32"
Horizontal Landing	Yes
Landing distance	5/16"
Leader extension	Yes
Text	—
Contents	09 29 00.D1 - 5/8"...
Text style	Arch-Dim
Justify	Left
Direction	Horizontal
Width	4'-0"
Height	1/32"

28. Select the **Reference Keynote (Straight Leader).**
Select the Insulation detail component.
Select the start and end point for the leader.
Set the text width to **4'0"**.
Press ENTER.
Select the text.
In the Height field, set the text height to **1/32"**.
Set the arrowhead size to 1/32".

29. Select the **Reference Keynote (Straight Leader).**
Select the Insulation detail component.
Select the start and end point for the leader.
Set the text width to **4'0"**.
Press ENTER.
Select the text.
In the Height field, set the text height to **1/32"**.
Set the arrowhead size to 1/32".

30. Select the **Reference Keynote (no leader).**

31. Select the Gypsum Board detail component.
Select the start and end point for the leader.
Set the text width to **6'-0"**.
Press ENTER.
Select the text.
In the Height field, set the text height to **1/32"**.
Set the arrowhead size to 1/32".

32. Set the current layer to A-Anno-Note.
Add a straight line to act as the leader for the gypsum board
keynote.

33. Scale and position the view title.

34. Select the **Reference Keynote Legend** tool on the Annotation tab.

35. Select the keynotes placed on the view.
Then select a point to the right of the view to place the legend.

36. Activate the **S1.2 Details** layout.

37. Activate the **Layout** ribbon.

Select the Rectangular viewport tool.

38. Draw a rectangle on the sheet to add a viewport.

Change the layer for the viewport to **Viewport.**

39.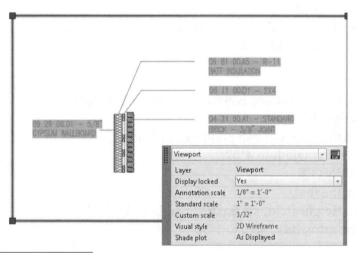

Position the detail wall view in the viewport.

Set the viewport scale to 1" = 1'0".

Lock the display.

40. Activate the **Layout** ribbon.

Select the Rectangular viewport tool.

41. Draw a rectangle on the sheet to add a viewport.

Change the layer for the viewport to **Viewport.**

42.

Position the reference keynotes legend in the viewport.
Set the Standard Scale to 1/8" = 1'-0".

Lock the display.

43. Return to the Model tab.
Update the attributes in the callout with the correct sheet number:
S1.2 and Detail Number: D12.

*If you do not see the view titles on the layout, type
ANNOALLVISIBLE and set to 1.*

44. Save as *ex8-11.dwg*.

Exercise 8-12
Creating Space Styles

Drawing Name: Ex8-11.dwg
Estimated Time: 10 minutes

1.   Open *ex8-11.dwg*.

2.   Activate the **Manage** ribbon.

                             Select the **Style Manager**.

3.   Locate the *Space Styles* drawing.

                             Make sure you set the Files of Type to dwg or you won't see it.

                             Note that there is only one space style currently available in the *ex8-12.dwg*.

4.   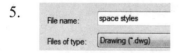   Select the **Open Drawing** tool.

5.   Browse to the exercise folders for this text.
      Change the files of type to **Drawing (*.dwg).**
      Open the *space styles.dwg*.

6. Expand the *space styles.dwg* in the Style Manager.

Note several space styles have been defined.

7. 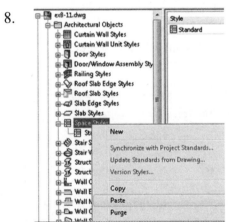 Highlight the **Space Styles** in the *space styles.dwg*.
Right click and select **Copy**.

8. Scroll up to the *ex8-11.dwg*.

Highlight **Space Styles**.

Right click and select **Paste**.

9. If this dialog appears advising of duplicate definitions:
Enable **Overwrite Existing**.
Press **OK**.

10. The space styles are now copied into your project.

Close the Style Manager.

11. Save as *ex8-12.dwg*.

Exercise 8-13
Adding Spaces

Drawing Name: Ex8-12.dwg
Estimated Time: 15 minutes

This exercise reinforces the following skills:

- ❑ Layouts
- ❑ Spaces

1.   Open *ex8-12.dwg*.

2.   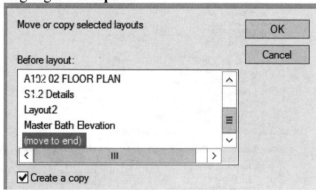 Right click on the layout tab and select **Move or Copy**.
Highlight **Floorplan**.

Enable **Create a copy**.

Highlight **(move to end)**.

Press **OK**.

3.   Select the second layout.

4. Highlight the second layout tab.

Right click and select **Rename**.

> Rename
> Move or Copy...
> Select All Layouts
> Activate Previous Layout
> Activate Model Tab
> Page Setup Manager...
> Plot...
> Drafting Standard Setup...
> Import Layout as Sheet...
> Export Layout to Model...
> Dock above Status Bar

5. Modify the layout name to **A102 03 ROOM PLAN**.

> etails \ A102 03 ROOM PLAN /

6. Double click inside the viewport to activate model space.

7. Select the **Generate Space** tool from the Home ribbon on the Build panel.

> Space ▼   Box
> Space
> Generate Space

8. On the Properties palette, select the space style to apply.

Left click inside the designated space to place the space.

> Style   Bathroom
> Name   Bathroom
> Tag   Bedroom
> Associative Closet
> Offset boundaries Den
> Create type Dining Room

9. If you hover over a space, you should see a tool tip with the space style name.

> Space
> Layer   A-Area-Spce
> Style Name Livingroom

10. Select a space.

In the Properties palette select the Name for the SPACE using the drop down list.

> Search...
> Style   Livingroom
> Name   Living Room
> Associative Yes
> Offset boundaries By style

This is the name that will appear on the room tag.

11. Repeat for all the spaces.
    Press ESC to release the selection of each space before moving on to the next space.

    Verify that only one space is selected to be renamed each time or you may assign a name to the wrong space unintentionally.

12. Save as *ex8-13.dwg*.

Exercise 8-14
Modifying Spaces

Drawing Name: Ex8-13.dwg
Estimated Time: 15 minutes

This exercise reinforces the following skills:

❑   Spaces

1.   Open *ex8-13.dwg*.

2.   Select the space located in the living room area.

3.   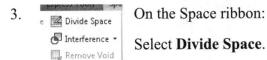 On the Space ribbon:

Select **Divide Space**.

4.   Place points to define a kitchen area.

5.   Repeat the Divide Space command to place lines to define the den and dining room areas.

Make sure each divided space is a closed polygon.

6.

Select the den area space.

Right click and select **Properties**.

Change the Style to **Den**.
Change the Name to **Den.**

Press **ESC** to release the selection.

7.

Select the kitchen area space.

Right click and select **Properties**.

Change the Style to **Kitchen**.
Change the Name to **Kitchen**.

Press **ESC** to release the selection.

8.

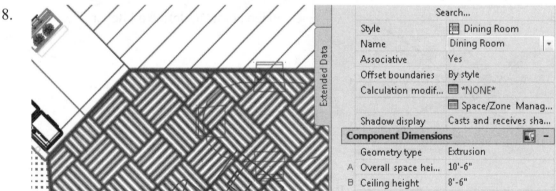

Select the dining room area space.

Right click and select **Properties**.

Change the Style to **Dining Room**.
Change the Name to **Dining Room**.

Press **ESC** to release the selection.

9. 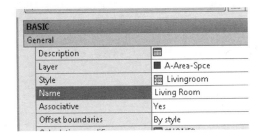 Select the Living room space.
Right click and select Properties.
On the Design tab:
Change the name to **Living Room**.

Repeat for the remaining spaces.

10. Select the section line used to define the wall section.

11. Set to **Hide in the current viewport** using the Layer drop-down on the Home ribbon.

12. Set A-**Sect-Iden** to **Hide in the current viewport**.

13. Inspect the floor plan to verify that all spaces have been placed.

Note that different space styles use different hatch patterns.

Freeze the A-Anno-Dims and A-Sect-Line layers in the current viewport.

14. Save as *ex8-14.dwg*.

Exercise 8-15
Adding Room Tags

Drawing Name: ex8-14.dwg
Estimated Time: 15 minutes

This exercise reinforces the following skills:

    ❑   Tags

1.   Open *ex8-14.dwg*.

2.   Select the **Tags** tab on the Document tool palette.

3.   Locate the **Room Tag (w/Dimensions)**.

4.   If you don't see the Room Tag (w/Dimensions) tool:

    Select **More Tag Tools** on the Tag tab of the tool palette.

5.   Run a search on room tag.

6.

Locate the **Room Tag (w/Dimensions)**.
Drag and drop on to the Tags palette.

7.

8.

Select the **A102 03 ROOM PLAN** layout tab.
Double click in the viewport to activate model space.

9.

Select the **Room Tag (w/Dimensions)**.

10.

Select the family room space.
Press **ENTER** to place the tag centered in the room.

11.

A small dialog will appear showing all the data attached to the space.

You can modify any field that is not grayed out.

Press **OK**.

12.

Repeat to tag all the spaces.

13.

Select the Hallway tag.

14.

On the Properties palette:
Select **Anchor**.

15. **Set the Rotation angle to 90.**
    Press OK.

16. Press ESC or left click outside the building model to release the selected tag.

17. The tag is rotated 90 degrees.

18. Save as *ex8-15.dwg*.

Exercise 8-16
Adding Door Tags

Drawing Name: ex8-15.dwg
Estimated Time: 15 minutes

This exercise reinforces the following skills:

  ❑ Tags

1. Open *ex8-15.dwg*.

2. ⟩ A102 02 Floor Plan ⟨S Activate the A102 02 Floor plan layout tab.

3. Activate model space by double-clicking inside the viewport.

4. Select the DEN space so it is highlighted.

5. 💡 ☼ 🗔 🔓 ■ A-Area-Spce
    💡 ☼ 🗔 🔓 ■ A-Area-Spce-Iden
    💡 ☼ 🗔 🔓 ■ A-Area-Spce-Patt

    Activate the Home ribbon.
    The A-Area-Spce layer should be shown.
    Freeze the layer in the current viewport.

6. Activate the Document palette.
   Activate the Tags tab.

   Select the Door Tag tool.

7.   Select a door.

   Press ENTER to center the tag on the door.

8.   Press **OK**.

Some students may be concerned because they see the Error getting value next to the Room Number field.

If you tag the spaces with a room tag assigning a number, you will not see that error.

9. Right click and select **Multiple**.
   Select the remaining doors in the floor plan to add the door tags.

10.   Press **OK.**

11. There are polylines which are used to divide the spaces.

12. Create a new layer called Space Dividing Lines.
Freeze in the current viewport.

13. Move the polylines onto the new layer.

14. Save as *ex8-16.dwg*.

Exercise 8-17

Create a Door Schedule

Drawing Name: ex8-16.dwg
Estimated Time: 10 minutes

This exercise reinforces the following skills:

□   Schedules

1. Open *ex8-16.dwg*.

2. ▶| Model / Work /   Activate the Model layout tab.

3. ▐▓▓ Door Schedule   Select the Door Schedule tool.

The Door Schedule tool can be found on the Annotate ribbon or on the Document tool palette on the Scheduling tab.

4. Window around the building model.

ACA will automatically filter out any non-door entities and collect only doors.

Press **ENTER**.

5.

DOOR AND FRAME SCHEDULE																	

Left click to place the schedule in the drawing window.

Press **ENTER**.

A ? will appear for any doors that are missing tags. So, if you see a ? in the list go back to the model and see which doors are missing tags.

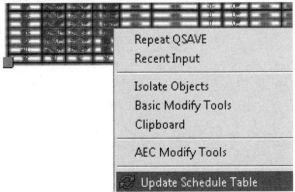

Repeat QSAVE
Recent Input

Isolate Objects
Basic Modify Tools
Clipboard

AEC Modify Tools

Update Schedule Table

Once you add door tags, you need to update the schedule. Select the schedule, right click and select Update Schedule Table.

6.   tion \ A102 02 Floor Plan \ S1.2 Details /   Activate the **A102 02 Floor Plan** layout tab.

7.   🗔 Rectangular ▾   Activate the Layout ribbon.
Select the **Rectangular** viewport tool.

8.   Draw a rectangular viewport.

Position the door schedule in the viewport.

9.

Viewport ▾	
Layer	Viewport
Display locked	Yes
Annotation scale	1/8" = 1'-0"
Standard scale	Custom
Custom scale	0"
Visual style	2D Wireframe
Shade plot	Hidden

Select the viewport.

Verify that it is on the Viewport layer.

Set the Standard scale to **Custom.**

Set the Display locked to **Yes**.

10. Save as *ex8-17.dwg*.

Exercise 8-18

Create a Door Schedule Style

Drawing Name: ex8-17.dwg
Estimated Time: 30 minutes

This exercise reinforces the following skills:

- ❑ Schedules
- ❑ Style Manager
- ❑ Text Styles
- ❑ Update Schedule

1. Open *ex8-17.dwg*.

2. | tion \ A102 02 Floor Plan / S1.2 Details /   Activate the **A102 02 Floor Plan** layout tab.

3. 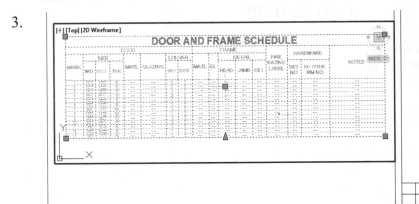   Double click inside the viewport with the door schedule.

    Select the schedule.

4.   Right click and select **Copy Schedule Table Style**.

    This will create a new style that you can modify.

5.   Select the **General** tab.

    Rename **Custom Door Schedule**.

6.   Select the **Columns** tab.

7. Highlight Louver, WD, and HGT.

8. Press **Delete**.

9. You will be asked to confirm the deletion.

   Press **OK**.

10.

    Highlight **MARK**.

    Select the **Add Column** button.

11.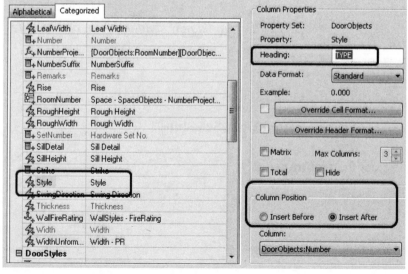

    Scroll down until you see Style.

    Highlight **Style**.

    Confirm that the Column Position will be inserted after the DoorObjects: Number.

    Change the Heading to **TYPE**.

    Press **OK**.

12.

	MARK	TYPE	
Property Set	DoorObjects	DoorObjects	Doo
Property	Number	Style	V
Format	Standard	Standard	Leng
Example	0.000	0.000	0
Total	No	No	
Hide	No	No	
Matrix	No	No	
Max Cols.			

The new column is now inserted.

13.

Table Title: DOOR SCHEDULE

Format

Title: ☑ Override Cell Format...

Column Headers: ☑ Override Cell Format...

Matrix Headers: ☐ Override Cell Format...

Select the Layout tab.

Change the Table Title to **DOOR SCHEDULE**.

14.

	SIZE			MATL
le	WD	HGT	THK	
bjects	DoorObjects	DoorObjects	DoorObjects	DoorStyles
le	Width	Height	Thickness	Material
dard	Length - Long	Length - Long	Length - Short	Case - Upper
	0	0	0	–
o	No	No	No	No
o	No	No	No	No
o	No	No	No	No

☐ Include Quantity Column

Formula Column... | Add Header... | Modify... |

Activate the Columns tab.

Highlight the **WD** column.

Select **Modify**.

15.

Column Properties

Property Set: DoorObjects
Property: Width
Heading: W
Data Format: Length - Long

Change the Heading to **W**.

Press **OK**.

16.

DOOR			
	SIZE		MATL
W	HGT	THK	
DoorObjects	DoorObjects	DoorObjects	DoorStyles
Width	Height	Thickness	Material
Length - Long	Length - Long	Length - Short	Case - Upper
0	0	0	–
No	No	No	No
No	No	No	No
No	No	No	No

☐ Include Quantity Column

la Column... | Add Header... | Modify... |

Highlight the **HGT** column.

Select **Modify**.

17.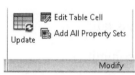

Change the Heading to **H**.

Press **OK**.

18. Press **OK** to close the dialog.

19.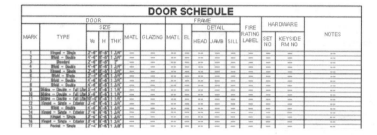

The schedule updates.

If there are question marks in the schedule, that indicates doors which remain untagged.

20.

Select the schedule.
Select **Update** from the ribbon.
Press **ESC** to release the selection.

21.

Activate the Home ribbon.

Select the **Text Style** tool on the Annotation panel.

22. RomanS
Schedule-Data
Schedule-Header
Schedule-Title

Notice there are text styles set up for schedules.
Highlight each one to see their settings.

23.

Highlight **Schedule-Data.**
Set the Font Name to **Arial Narrow**.
Enable **Annotative**.

Press **Apply**.

24.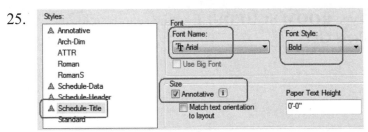
    Highlight Schedule-Header.
    Set the Font Name to **Arial**.
    Set the Font Style to **Bold**.
    Enable **Annotative**.

    Press **Apply**.

25.
    Highlight Schedule-Title.
    Set the Font Name to **Arial**.
    Set the Font Style to **Bold**.
    Enable **Annotative**.

    Press **Apply** and **Close**.

26. Note that the schedule automatically updates.

MARK	Style	SIZE			MATL	GLAZING	
		W	H	THK			
1	Hinged - Single	1010	2000	40	--		
2	Hinged - Single	1010	2000	40	--		
3	Hinged - Single	1010	2000	40	--		
4	Bifold - Double	1500	2100	40	--		

27. Save as *ex8-18.dwg*.

Exercise 8-19

Create a Room Schedule

Drawing Name: ex8-18.dwg
Estimated Time: 30 minutes

This exercise reinforces the following skills:

- Schedules
- Tool Palettes
- Content Browser
- Schedule Styles

1. Open *ex8-18.dwg*.

2. Activate the Model layout tab.

3. Activate the **DOCUMENT** palette.
   Scroll down to the bottom of the Schedules tab.

   Select **More Scheduling Tools**.

4. Type **ROOM SCHEDULE** in the search field.
   Press **GO**.

5. Locate the Room Schedule.
   Drag and drop onto the Schedules palette.

6. Select Room Schedule from the palette.

7. Window around the building model.
   Press ENTER.
   Pick to place the schedule.
   Press ENTER.

8. Select the schedule.
   Right click and select **Edit Schedule Table Style**.

9. Highlight **ROOM NAME** and select **Add Column**.

10. Highlight **Style**.
    Change the Heading to **ROOM NAME**.
    Enable **Insert before**.

    Press **OK**.

11. Highlight the column that uses the SpaceObjects:Name.

Press **Delete**.

12. Press **OK**.

13. Highlight the **ROOM NAME** column.

Press **Modify**.
Change the Data Format to **Case-Upper**.

Place a check next to Total.

Press **OK** twice.

14. The schedule updates.

15. Select the schedule.
Right click and select **Edit Schedule Table Style**.

16. Select the **Sorting/Grouping** tab.
Highlight **Sort**.
Select the **Add** button.
Select **SpaceStyles:Style** to sort by Style name.
Press **OK**.

17. Place a check next to **Group**.
Place a check next to Display Subtotals for **Group.**

Press **OK** to close the dialog.

18.

The schedule updates.

19.

Select the schedule.
Right click and select **Edit Schedule Table Style**.

20.

Highlight the **AREA** column.

Press **Modify**.

21.

Place a check next to **Total**.

Press **OK.**

22.

Save as *ex8-19.dwg*.

QUIZ 4

True or False

1. Columns, braces, and beams are created using Structural Members.

2. When you isolate a Layer User Group, you are freezing all the layers in that group.

3. You can isolate a Layer User Group in ALL Viewports, a Single Viewport, or a Selection Set of Viewports.

4. When placing beams, you can switch the justification in the middle of the command.

5. Standard AutoCAD commands, like COPY, MOVE, and ARRAY cannot be used in ACA.

Multiple Choice

6. Before you can place a beam or column, you must:

    A. Generate a Member Style
    B. Activate the Structural Member Catalog
    C. Select a structural member shape
    D. All of the above

7. Select the character that is OK to use when creating a Structural Member Style Name.

    A. -
    B. ?
    C. =
    D. /

8. Identify the tool shown.

    A. Add Brace
    B. Add Beam
    C. Add Column
    D. Structural Member Catalog

9. Setting a Layer Key

    A. Controls which layer AEC objects will be placed on.
    B. Determines the layer names created.
    C. Sets layer properties.
    D. All of the above.

10. There are two types of stairs used in residential buildings:

    A. INSIDE and OUTSIDE
    B. METAL and WOOD
    C. MAIN and SERVICE
    D. FLOATING and STATIONARY

11. Select the stair type that does not exist from the list below:

    A. Straight-run
    B. M Stairs
    C. L Stairs
    D. U Stairs

12. The first point selected when placing a set of stairs is:

    A. The foot/bottom of the stairs B.
    The head/top of the stairs
    C. The center point of the stairs
    D. Depends on the property settings

ANSWERS:

1) T; 2) F; 3) T; 4) T; 5) F; 6) D; 7) A; 8) A; 9) A; 10) C; 11) B; 12) D